Richard L. Goodman

Classical Chinese Medical Texts

Learning to Read the Classics of Chinese Medicine

Windstone Press

www.windstonepress.com

Classical Chinese Medical Texts:
Learning to Read the Classics of Chinese Medicine
ISBN-13: 978-0-9823212-0-1
ISBN-10: 0-9823212-0-1

Author: Richard L. Goodman

English Editor: Phoebe James

Chinese editing and cover design: Chen Shih-i

Printed in the United States of America

10 9 8 7 6 5 4 3 2 1

Version 1.0

Contents

Acknowledgments

This book would not have been possible without the prodding of those who have pushed me to write something for many years. Others have encouraged me over the last year to finish this manuscript. Among these people are Denise Andersen, David Chard, Luc Chen, Liz and Sean Diesel, Sean Tuten, and Phoebe James, who also edited and offered invaluable comments on the entire manuscript.

I have benefited from numerous great teachers of Chinese medicine, language, history, and literature. Dr. Lynsay Tunnel was an early inspiration during my training in Chinese medicine. While studying in Taipei at National Taiwan Normal University, I was fortunate enough to learn from Lu Cui-ying, who is one of the most skilled teachers I have learned from. Her teaching methods influenced the approach to Chinese used in this book. Additionally, the funding I received from the Centre for East Asian Studies at the Chinese University of Hong Kong for research in the history of Chinese medicine exposed me to aspects of scholarship I would not have otherwise encountered.

Over the last decade, it has been my good fortune to be surrounded by highly knowledgeable professionals and academics who were willing to share their knowledge with me. While the help and encouragement I have received is at the heart of this book, any errors or omissions are mine alone.

Preface

Learning to read the classics of Chinese medicine is a daunting task. Many students and practitioners of this medicine never expend the energy required to gain mastery of the language. Over the last few years, a number of classical Chinese textbooks have become available, making the language much more accessible.[1] For those interested in only medical texts, however, studying such books requires the memorization of hundreds of characters that will never show up in medicine before medical texts can be approached. While great benefit can be gained from reading across fields to better understand the culture and historical period of any text, this is usually not the medical reader's first priority. This book was written to build a bridge into classical medical texts for those who have found taking the leap far too time consuming and frustrating.

Chinese is a difficult language in both its modern and classical forms. This book aims to wipe out the unnecessary difficulties in learning to read classical medical texts while also acknowledging that reading classical Chinese is a difficult task. Learning to look at Chinese characters instead of English letters is challenging, as is learning to understand the often-times simplistically difficult grammar patterns. One of the biggest problems in understanding a text is the appearance of statements that seem vague or unclear. A novice reader's first instinct is to try to figure out every detail of even the simplest statements, resulting in missing the main idea of the text. Allowing the simplicity of the text is often more effective for understanding its meaning.

Another common approach, also taken by novices, is to translate a sentence or text and then try to understand it through their translation. The purpose of this book is to teach people to read the classics of Chinese medicine and is not intended to teach readers how to translate classical medical texts. Translations of classical Chinese works, related to medicine or other subjects, can be beautiful representations of the originals which add to the understanding of the field they represent. They can also be horrible misrepresentations which actually damage the field they are meant to help. There are, unfortunately, very few examples of medical texts that represent the original Chinese well.[2]

Even translations that include the original Chinese do not provide a good way to learn classical Chinese; in fact, the better a translation is into English, the worse it could be for learning the language.[3] English translations of classical Chinese never fully represent the meaning of the original Chinese in a way that suits language learners. For example, the meanings of the *empty characters*[4] vary in context so much that they cannot be translated in a consistent way. Trying to understand a text without knowing how such characters function would be impossible.

When Westerners first began reading classical Chinese, there were no textbooks and few translations existed. At that time, those studying the language were academics who spent countless hours in libraries comparing translations. They had language teachers to help them with grammar and professors who could provide interpretations. They also became fluent in modern Chinese and could read modern Chinese translations of classical Chinese texts.[5] While learning modern Chinese first so that one can learn to read translations into that language is probably the best method for learning to read classical texts, most people are not going to make the commitment to move to Asia for a few years so that they can grasp the language enough to read modern Chinese. This being the case, there is still no reason to continue to compare translations with the Chinese until the reader has a gained a sufficient understanding of classical grammar and a firm grasp of several hundred commonly used Chinese characters.

The translations in this book are meant to serve as a guide to understanding the Chinese. Translations are too often taken to be the *final* word. Some translators take a strong stance on the meaning of a text in the target language. Most classical Chinese sentences can be translated in a number of ways and still represent the meaning of the original text. Understanding the selections presented in this book will be much easier if the focus moves away from the translation toward the Chinese itself. Understanding the vocabulary and grammar sections before reading the translation will help readers become more focused on the meaning of the Chinese. The translation can be referenced to better understand how the selection comes together.

Over the past several years, practitioners of Chinese medicine and linguists from various backgrounds have debated the consistency of translation to ensure the usefulness of the material. Those who are interested in learning to read classical Chinese language need not focus on details of how individual characters are rendered into English. One's native language, in this case English, can serve as a useful guide to learning Chinese, but the English translation will never be equivalent to the Chinese character. On the other hand, a standard terminology such as the one developed by Nigel Wiseman is helpful to those students who will never study classical Chinese medical texts.[6] In this spirit, I have used Wiseman's terminology when I believe it best represents the meaning of the character in context. In the glossary and vocabulary sections, I have tried to use as many of the common English representations of characters as I can without causing confusion. I take responsibility for any confusion resulting in my choice of terms.

Book Contents

Each of the fifteen chapters has six major sections. The first page of each chapter is separated for easier review. The text on this page reads from right to left, and up to down, just as classical Chinese was written.

The second page always begins with a modern, easy to read version of the text with the corresponding pinyin below it. The characters are read from left to right, just as English and modern Chinese is now written. The introductory chapters include a direct translation into English. This "translation" is grammatically incorrect in English and is meant to reflect the Chinese meaning as closely as possible.

The **Vocabulary** section follows this so that it can be easily referenced when reading the text on the second page. The definitions include the meaning of the character in the context of that chapter. Other common definitions, some of which do not appear in that chapter but might appear in a later chapter are also included. A character covered in a previous chapter is never covered again in the vocabulary section, making it essential to master the vocabulary for each chapter before moving on to the next. The pinyin is always included in the texts and example sentences so readers can easily find characters in the pinyin index.

The **Notes** section is used for explanations of grammar, difficult sentences, and to clarify any potentially confusing areas. Those with a background in linguistics might take issue with these explanations.[7] Simple explanation has been favored over rigid linguistic terminology. In some chapters, complicated sentences and terms are broken down further and explained. Becoming very familiar with the contents of this section is the most important key to interpreting passages correctly.

The **Translation** of each chapter's text is purposely placed away from the Chinese text. The translation is meant be the least referenced part of each chapter. Focusing on the translation will keep beginners from making the switch from relying on English to reading Chinese. While debates about how something might be better translated into English are not useful in learning to read texts, discussing the meaning of the Chinese in any language will help learners stay focused on the Chinese.

The last section of each chapter is the **Character Focus** section. A single character is discussed at length to give readers a deeper view into the meanings and uses of Chinese characters.

The Appendices in the back of this book are for reference. Appendix I contains a simplified Chinese version of the selections from all fifteen Chapters. This simplified Chinese system was created in the People's Republic of China during the 1950's in order to encourage literacy and are worth knowing for two reasons. First, a few simplified characters are based on more ancient forms and will sometimes appear in original texts. Second, a few mainland Chinese publishing companies are now making many classical texts available in simplified Chinese. Many of these books include the source text, translation into modern Chinese, and commentaries on the texts. This book focuses on traditional characters because the original texts pre-dating the 20th century do not use the simplified Character system and any medical text written before this time is easier to find in its original traditional version.

Appendix II provides more information on some of the texts selected for this book. Appendix III is a **Glossary** alphabetized by English meaning. The most common nouns and verbs are included here, but because many grammar particles have no common English meaning out of context, they are not included.

The **Pinyin Index** is used to list all of the characters used in this book. Included in each listing is the English meaning, location of the character in the vocabulary listing by chapter, and page numbers for any mention of the character in the **Notes** section. If a character appears within a later text, but has no mention in the Notes section, an additional page number is not given.

Each chapter has been selected from a variety of medical texts ranging from the late Han to Qing dynasties, spanning a period of about 1,500 years. The selections from later periods are often easier to grasp, likely due to a more systematized style of writing. Some involved in Chinese medicine prefer older texts, such as the *Nei Jing*, and resist evaluating works written after the Tang Dynasty. This will lead to problems in understanding the earlier texts, as the commentaries by later authors offer the only chance to compare interpretations over time. Without access to these later commentaries, readers will find some parts of earlier texts impossible to understand through the language of those texts alone.

The texts in this book have been selected with beginning language learner's needs in mind. They follow a theme of fire, the triple warmer, and the heart protector with a couple of exceptions. Additionally, these texts were selected due to their subject matter having been debated over time. Many of these texts point out some of the major inconsistencies between modern "Traditional Chinese Medicine" and classical texts. With the exception of Chapter Nine, all of these texts are partial pieces of a chapter from the given text, leaving out big pieces of contextual information; therefore, this book is in no way intended to be used in a clinical setting.

Unit One: The first two chapters contain sentences and phrases selected from a variety of medical texts. These sayings can all be found throughout medical literature and contain some of the most important characters and grammar particles needed for reading medical texts. Chapter Three is from a passage written by Zhao Xian-ke during the Ming Dynasty. Zhao believed that the *life gate*, which he said is between the two kidneys, was the true ruler of the body and proposed indirect evidence from the *Nei Jing* to back up his claims. This text contains a small portion of how he saw the body's physiology. Chapter Four contains an excerpt from the prolific medical writer Xu Ling-tai's *Yi Guan Bian*. Passages very similar to this one can be found in a variety of Ming and Qing dynasty medical texts.

Unit Two: This unit contains three excerpts from the *Nan Jing*, one entire chapter of the same text (Chapter Nine), and two excerpts from the *Nei Jing Su Wen*. The *Nan Jing* was likely written around the end of the Han Dynasty. This work is usually attributed to Bian Que, but true authorship is unknown. While often considered a work explaining complicated issues within the *Nei Jing*, the contents reflect a distinct view and often contradict the *Nei Jing*. The passages selected clarify many of these contradictions and allow distinctions to be made regarding how concepts such as the triple warmer and the heart master have changed since the writing of the *Nan Jing*.

The selections from the *Su Wen* in chapters Seven and Ten of this book were probably written by different authors separated by hundreds of years.[8] The selection in Chapter Seven comes from what is now called Chapter 23 of the *Su Wen*. This section gives correspondences that are still memorized by students today. Chapter Ten of this book corresponds to what is now called Chapter 71 of the *Su Wen*.

This unit ends with another selection from Xu Ling-tai and his discussion of the disease known as being *struck by wind*. In most Qing Dynasty medical texts that discuss specific disorders, this is the first disease discussed. This is not the disease that is equated with the common cold, but a range of serious afflictions ranging from sudden paralysis, to coma, and even stroke.

Unit Three contains the final four chapters. These are the only chapters that split one author's writings into separate chapters. This section is taken from the *Enlightened Heart of*

Medical Studies. This work has received almost no attention in the West, even though its structure would be recognized by students of modern TCM. These four chapters give the reader a chance to follow Cheng Guo-peng's explanation and interpretation of a previous author's statements, which is a useful skill in interpreting classical texts. Cheng also makes use of analogy, which becomes a common feature of Qing Dynasty texts.

Upon finishing this book, readers will walk away with a strong grasp of classical Chinese medical texts. Becoming fluent in these texts is a life-long work. Those who are serious about learning how to read classical medical texts will find they need an ever expanding tool chest to work from. There are plenty of free tools available to help in this endeavor. Our website offers tips and resources for the learner who wants to continue learning to read Chinese medical texts.

How to Use This Book

Those learning in the classroom and those engaged in self-study are encouraged to approach this book with the method outlined below. This method maximizes the learner's ability to make the necessary switch from reading and relying on English to focusing on Chinese characters and grammar patterns. Everyone learns differently, so modifying the method may work for some. However, this is a highly effective way to learn to read Chinese. The most important part of this method is to **read the translation only after the vocabulary and grammar have been studied**. The translation can be a guide, but must be the least referenced part of each chapter. Native English readers' brains need to make a shift in order to learn Chinese. This takes time and the impulse to read the translation first should be resisted.

1. Review all of the vocabulary for the chapter. Focus on each character and its English meaning. The pinyin was added to benefit those who have already studied modern Mandarin Chinese and makes the pinyin index an extremely useful tool. Every vocabulary listing in this book is commonly found in Chinese medical texts, making each character in this book valuable to the learner. For those who have *not* studied modern Chinese, the pinyin pronunciation may be memorized after the entire book is studied and all of the characters are recognized

Most learners find it helpful to write individual characters. Those who can write a given character can easily recognize that character in a text. Spending a lot of time with the vocabulary section first will make reading the text easier. I highly suggest making flashcards and memorizing all of the characters before moving on to the next section.

2. Read the notes section once. Read the example sentences, but do not spend a lot of time trying to understand the details at this point. Notice that you haven't even approached the text yet. By first learning the vocabulary and then giving yourself an overview of the grammar, approaching the text will be much easier and encourage you to keep learning.

3. Read the text from the second page of each chapter. Read the entire selection once without referencing any vocabulary or grammar notes to see which characters are causing difficulty. Read it again and reference the vocabulary section for the characters that are proving difficult to remember.

4. Now study the notes section in-depth. Read all of the example sentences and be sure the meaning of each character is understood. Reference the index and vocabulary sections when needed. Write any regularly forgotten characters over and over. The example sentences were created from the grammar and vocabulary words already studied. These sentences are only there to reinforce vocabulary and grammar patterns and are not a continuation of the chapter's main text.

5. Read the passage from the second page again and then read the translation at the end of each chapter. The translation is as direct as possible while still maintaining

grammatically correct English. Then go back to the passage and read it again, noting any places that are still unclear. Take advantage of the index to look up complicated words or grammar patterns.

6. When the text is fully understood, read the Character Focus section, which is an overview of one of the more important characters covered. This section will help those not familiar with Chinese characters understand how the meanings can be seen from within the character.

7. Read the Chinese from the first page of each previously studied chapter. This page was designed for review and contains no English translation or pinyin. It also reflects how a text looks in most reproductions of Chinese classics. The characters in this section are written in a slightly different style. Some characters will be difficult to recognize while others will look almost the same. Chinese characters are written differently depending on time period, author, and writing or printing styles. This section addresses the need to read characters in a variety of formats.

8. Move on to the next chapter only when the first page of each previously studied chapter can be read without referencing the glossary or grammar notes. Review previously studied chapters before beginning a new study session. This book assumes that readers have mastered one chapter before moving on to the next. Constantly reviewing page one of each chapter is the best way to gain mastery of the material.

9. Visit our website to find discussion forums about difficult areas. Here, there will be opportunities to clarify the meanings of difficult characters or grammar notes.

Notes

[1] The best of these is Edwin G. Pulleyblank's *Outline of Classical Chinese Grammar* (UBC Press, 1995). This book is highly recommended for those who want detailed linguistic explanations of grammar.

[2] As of this writing, only two translations that represent the original Chinese well exist. The first is Nigel Wiseman's translation of the 傷寒論 (shāng hán lùn) titled *Shang Han Lun* (Paradigm Publications, 1999). The other is Paul Unschuld's translation of the 難經 (nán jīng) titled *The Classic of Difficult Issues* (University of California Press, 1986).

[3] For a good example of this, see Chapter Six, note six. Paul Unschuld translates this line as, "One of the conduits encompasses the hand-minor-yin (vessel) and the heart-master (vessel) as separate vessels." There is nothing wrong with this translation; however, if a reader has no understanding of the grammar or vocabulary and then compares this sentence with the Chinese, there is little chance any insight into the meaning of the Chinese could be gained. Learners who use even good translations will encounter this problem.

[4] The term *empty character refers* to 虛字 (xū zì). These grammar particles are without meanings on their own, but still change the overall meaning of the sentence they appear in. The most frequently used 虛字 are 之, 者, 而, and 也, all of which are covered in this text.

[5] Those new to classical Chinese often do not realize that it is a distinct language from modern Chinese. Native speakers of Chinese cannot read it unless they have been specifically trained. Many novices assume that because classical and modern Chinese share characters that those who are raised with Chinese as their mother tongue can read classical Chinese. This is like thinking Americans

---

can read German because English and German share an alphabet. Those wanting to learn how to read classical Chinese need to look to teachers who have been specifically trained in the language.

[6] Nigel Wiseman's *Practical Dictionary of Chinese Medicine* (Paradigm Publications, 1999) is the basis for Wiseman's terminology. The early terminology debate was fruitful and clarified a lot of issues. In recent years, this debate has stopped serving how we speak about Chinese medicine. Wiseman's dictionary is still the best guide for understanding how Chinese medical terminology is best rendered into English.

[7] For those who want a great guide to the grammar of classical Chinese written by an astute linguist, see note one.

[8] For a complete history of the changes in the text of the *Inner Classic*, see Paul Unschuld's *Huang Di Nei Jing Su Wen: Nature, Knowledge, Imagery in an Ancient Chinese Medical Text* (University of California Press, 2003)

Unit One

Chapter One

醫小道也
醫之治病也
從陰陽則生

1. 醫小道也。
   yī xiǎo dào yě.
   medicine small path
2. 醫之治病也。
   yī zhī zhìbìng yě.
   physicians they treat disease
3. 從陰陽則生。
   cóng yīn yáng zé shēng.
   follow yin-yang then life

Vocabulary

1.	醫	yī	medicine, physician
2.	小	xiǎo	small, lesser, insignificant
	大	dà	big, greater
3.	道	dào	The Way, a path
4.	也	yě	an end particle
5.	之	zhī	possessive marker nominalizer him, her, it, they
6.	治	zhì	to cure, to treat, to control
7.	病	bìng	illness, sickness
8.	從	cóng	from, by means of to follow, to accompany
9.	陰陽	yīn yáng	yin and yang

10. 則	zé	then (if. . . then. . .) contrastive particle
11. 生	shēng	life to give birth, grow, generate
死	sǐ	death to die

Notes

1. 也 This character is an end particle used to emphasize a statement. While this character is not grammatically the same as the English verb *to be*, it often performs a similar function. This character is placed after the subject and object and not between them, as is the English verb *to be*. The formula AB+也 in classical Chinese means *A is B* when no other verb is present. Note that A and B can range from simple words to longer ideas which appear to be sentences themselves.

Examples:

a. 陰小也。
yīn xiǎo yě.
Yin is small.

b. 陽大也。
yáng dà yě.
Yang is big.

c. 小道大道也。
xiǎo dào dà dào yě.
The lesser path is the greater path.

2. 之 has three major functions, two of which occur in the next chapter. In the second sentence, 之 is a pronoun referring to a previously mentioned noun. In this case, because the only preceding word is *physician* (醫), it must be referring to this. Here, the purpose of 之 is to accentuate the subject. Directly translated into English, this sentence means *Physicians, they treat disease.* In the *Nei Jing*, using 之 in this way is very common. The formula noun + 之 + verb (object) + (也) helps to distinguish this usage from the others outlined in Chapter Two.

3. 則 This character means *if...then*. The conditions in the clause before 則 are required before the second clause can be realized. This character connects cause and effect.
Examples:
a. 從小道則死。
cóng xiǎo dào zé sǐ.
If the minor path is followed, then death (occurs).

b. 治病則生。
zhì bìng zé shēng.
If the illness is treated, then life (continues).

In direct translation, the first example above would read *If follow minor path then death.* Classical Chinese often makes more simple statements and would not use the word *occurs*. Similarly, the second example uses the English word *continues*, which is not in the original Chinese. In classical Chinese language, *If treat illness then live* is clear.

Translation

1. Medicine is a lesser path.
2. Physicians, they treat illness.
3. If Yin and Yang are followed, then life (continues).

醫

The character for medicine uses 殹 as a phonetic. The enclosed character 矢 represents arrows in a quiver and when combined with 殳, the meaning is the sound made when an arrow leaves its quiver. In ancient times, it was thought that this sound resembled the sounds of the sick. The lower character 酉 is a pictograph of a wine cask.

Chapter Two

三焦者水鼓之道路也
身有表裏上下之別焉

1. 三焦者水鼓之道路也。
   sān jiāo zhě shuǐ gǔ zhī dàolù yě.
   triple burner (is) water-grain's passageway
2. 身有表裏上下之別焉。
   shēn yǒu biǎo lǐ shàng xià zhī bié yān.
   body has (exterior interior upper lower)'s distinction in it

---

Vocabulary

1.	三焦	sān jiāo	triple burner, triple warmer
2.	者	zhě	one who, those who
3.	水鼓	shuǐ gǔ	water & grains, food & water
4.	道路	dào lù	pathway
5.	路	lù	a road
6.	身	shēn	body
7.	有	yǒu	to have
	無	wú	to not have
8.	表	biǎo	exterior
9.	裏	lǐ	interior
10.	上	shàng	up, above, upper to go up, to ascend

11.	下	xià	down, below, lower to go down, to descend
	中	zhōng zhòng	center, middle to be struck by (a pathogen)
12.	別	bié	distinction, difference
13.	焉	yān	short for 於之(in it)
	於	yú	preposition (in, on, at, etc.)

Notes

1. In Chapter One, 之 was used as a pronoun referring back to the subject. In sentence one above, 之 serves as a possessive marker, as *apostrophe s* and the word *of* does in English. In sentence one above, 水鼓之道路 means *the path of water and grains.*

Examples:

a. 三焦之水穀
   sān jiāo zhī shuǐ gǔ
   triple burner's water and grains
   the water and grains of the triple burner

b. 陰陽之道路
   yīn yáng zhī dào lù
   yin and yang's path
   the path of yin and yang

c. 病之陰陽
   bìng zhī yīn yáng
   the yin and yang (distinctions) of illness

The third example of using 之 occurs in sentence two above, where it connects more than one noun. In this case, 表裏上 and 下 are all connected to 別. This use of 之 is not functionally much different from the possessive meaning. Sentence two means *The body* (身) *has* (有) *distinctions* (別) *of* (之) *exterior/ interior* (表裏) *upper/ lower* (上下) *in it* (焉).

Examples:

a. 表之病
   biǎo zhī bìng
   an exterior illness

b. 三焦有上中下之別焉。
   sān jiāo yǒu shàng zhōng xià zhī bié yān.
   The triple burner has distinctions of upper, middle, (and) lower within it.
   Classical Chinese often uses lists of nouns in combination (as in 上中下 above) without punctuation or conjunctions. These groups can be followed by 之 to connect them with another noun.

c. 身無大小之別焉。
   shēn wú dà xiǎo zhī bié yān.
   The body has no distinctions of lesser or greater within it.

d. 醫有陰陽之別焉。
   yī yǒu yīn yáng zhī bié yān.
   Medicine has distinctions of yin and yang within it.

Sentence two can be broken down to distinguish the parts of grammar:

身有別	the body has distinctions
身有別焉	the body has distinctions within it
身有表裏之別焉	the body has distinctions of interior (and) exterior within it

2. 者 This character has multiple uses and is therefore impossible to translate as a single character. In sentence one, the character 者 makes it clear that the preceding characters (三焦) are a noun. Often, the characters preceding 者 are clearly nouns. In such cases, 者 is placed to emphasize that this noun is the subject of the sentence. When used in this way, the sentence is ended with the character 也. In later chapters, there will be examples of adjectives and verbs being nominalized (turned into nouns) by 者.

When an action precedes 者, it usually means *those who* (see Chapter Eleven, 學者 xué zhě). Interpreting 者 can be tricky at first, so memorizing all of the potential meanings will be important for future reference.

Examples:

a. 從陰陽者
cóng yīn yáng zhě
those who follow yin and yang

b. 從道者
cóng dào zhě
those who follow the Way

c. 治病者醫也。
zhì bìng zhě yī yě.
Those who treat illness are physicians.

3. 焉 The character 焉 is a one character representation of the characters 於之 (in it, yú zhī). This character is placed at the end of a clause and can usually be thought of as *in it* or *within it*. This character functions much like 之 in Chapter One. To determine what 焉 is referring to, look to the preceding characters.

Examples:

a. 身有別焉。

shēn yǒu bié yān.

The body has distinctions within it.

b. 病有表裏之別焉。

bìng yǒu biǎo lǐ zhī bié yān.

Illness has the distinctions of exterior and interior within it.

Translation

1. The Triple Burner is the passageway of water and grains.
2. The body has distinctions of exterior, interior, upper and lower within it.

This character is used in a variety of contexts, from Confucian texts on governing, to philosophy, to cosmology, and even medicine. This is the character made famous by the 道德經 (dào dé jīng) by 老子 (Lǎo Zi). The upper or right part of this character is 首, which contains a pictograph of the face plus hair on top. This represents the head and usually refers to the *head*, *top*, or *first* in a group. On the left or bottom is the radical for movement (辶). Within this character, this represents movement toward the furthest visible point—the path always contains something in front of the traveler that comes to a head, or a point, off in the distance.

Chapter Three

有命門然後生心心主血
有心然後生肺肺主皮毛
有肺然後生腎腎主骨髓
有腎則與命門合二數

1. 有命門然後生心。心主 血。
   yǒu mìng mén rán hòu shēng xīn. xīn zhǔ xuè.
   there is Life-gate then generate heart. heart rule blood
2. 有心然後生肺。肺主皮毛。
   yǒu xīn rán hòu shēng fèi. fèi zhǔ pí máo.
   there is heart then generate lung. lung rule skin / hair
3. 有肺然後生腎。腎主骨髓。
   yǒu fèi rán hòu shēng shèn. shèn zhǔ gǔ suǐ.
   there is lung then generate kidney. kidney rule bone marrow
4. 有腎則與命門合二數。
   yǒu shèn zé yǔ mìng mén hé èr shǔ.
   there is kidney then with life gate combine twice

Vocabulary

1.	有	yǒu	there is, there are, there exists
2.	命門	mìng mén	life gate, gate of life
	命	mìng	life, fate, destiny, decree, order to order
	門	mén	gate, door
3.	然	rán	(to be) like this, however
4.	後	hòu	after, behind
5.	然後	rán hòu	only then
6.	心	xīn	heart, heart-mind

7.	主	zhǔ	to rule, to govern
8.	血	xiě, xuè	blood
9.	肺	fèi	lung
10.	皮	pí	skin
11.	毛	máo	body hair, hair
12.	腎	shèn	kidney
	肝	gān	liver
	脾	pí	spleen
13.	骨髓	gǔ suǐ	bone marrow
	骨	gǔ	bone(s)
	髓	suǐ	marrow
14.	與	yǔ	and, with, together with to give, to accompany
15.	合	hé	combine, mix together
16.	二	èr	two
	兩	liǎng	two
17.	數	shù	number
		shǔ	to count, to figure

Notes

1. In Chapter Two, the phrase 身有 was easy to interpret as *the body has*. In this chapter, 有 begins the sentence in absence of a subject. In this case, 有 means *there are*.

At times 有 is combined with the character 者, meaning *there are those who* (有...者). 者 can also combine with 無 to mean *there are none who* (無...者).
Examples:
a. 有從道者
yǒu cóng dào zhě
there are those who follow the Way

b. 無從陰陽者
wú cóng yīn yáng zhě
there are none who follow yin and yang

c. 有治病者
yǒu zhì bìng zhě
there are those who treat illness

2. 然後 is another way of saying *then*, although the emphasis is quite different from 則 as seen in Chapter One. These two characters are focusing on a sequence of events and relate to time, whereas 則 is more situational. Literally, 然後 means *like this, then after*.

3. 有...然後 In this pattern, the noun(s) or conditions after 有 need to exist first. The first sentence of this text reads 有命門然後生心. This sentence means that the life gate exists, and only thereafter can the heart be generated. The author of this

text sees the life gate as the first condition for the generation of all other organs within the body.

Examples:

a. 有身然後生病。

yǒu shēn rán hòu shēng bìng.

There is a body (and) then disease is generated.
(there cannot be disease without a body for it to occur in)

b. 有病然後生醫。

yǒu bìng rán hòu shēng yī.

There is disease (and) then medicine is created (born).
(medicine was only developed after disease came about)

c. 有陰陽然後有別。

yǒu yīn yáng rán hòu yǒu bié.

There is yin and yang (and) then there are distinctions.
(distinctions are only possible because there are opposites, such as yin and yang, to compare)

4. 則 Note that in sentence four, the character 則 seems to be missing a first clause whereby the English word *if* would fit. In such a case, this character can simply be thought of as *then* without any thought of a dependant first clause. There may be a hint of contrastive quality in 則 in this sentence (see Chapter Twelve, Note 1).

5. 與 is a conjunction meaning *with* or *and*. In the passage above, 與 appears with a noun on either side, linking the two nouns so as to later categorize them. This character is not placed between all nouns like the English word *and*, but is mostly used for comparisons or when the link between two nouns needs to be made clear. In this case, 腎 and 命門 are separated, so 與 is used to clarify their link. This character can

also be a verb meaning *to give* or *to accompany*, which becomes important for understanding its use in Chapter Six.

6. The characters 二 and 兩 need to be differentiated to understand how each character is used to represent *two*. 二 is used to represent the number two, the second in a series, or *twice*. In contrast, 兩 is employed when counting two items and is followed by a noun that can be counted. 二數 could be interpreted as *counting as two*, but 兩數 would be interpreted as *two numbers*. Note that only the number two uses two characters for different purposes, but sometimes 二 can be used in the same way as 兩, but not vice versa. All of the other numbers can perform any of the functions distinguished by 二 and 兩.

一	二	兩	三	四	五	六	七	八	九	十
yī	èr	liǎng	sān	sì	wǔ	liù	qī	bā	jiǔ	shí
1	2	2	3	4	5	6	7	8	9	10

Translation

1. There is the life gate, and only then the heart is generated. The heart rules the blood.
2. There is the heart, and only then the lung is generated. The lung rules the skin and body hair.
3. There is the lung, and only then the kidney is generated. The kidney rules the bones and marrow.
4. There is the kidney, (and it) then combines with the life gate, counting as two.

The main part of this character is a modified 令 (lìng), which means *decree* or *order*. On the lower left part is 口, meaning mouth. While it has become popular in recent years to focus on the English word *destiny* as the meaning of this character, its use in a variety of contexts makes a narrow translation impossible. In most texts, including medical, the interpretation of this character as destiny does not make sense. Order, command, life, fate, and destiny, among others, are all possible interpretations.

Chapter Four

有陽火有陰火有水中之火有土中之火有金中之火有木中之火陽火者天上之日月之火陰火者虛火此對待之火也

1. 有陽火，有陰火。有水中之火，有土中之火。有金中之火，有木中之火。
   yǒu yáng huǒ, yǒu yīn huǒ. yǒu shuǐ zhōng zhī huǒ, yǒu tǔ zhōng zhī huǒ. yǒu jīn zhōng zhī huǒ, yǒu mù zhōng zhī huǒ.
   there is yang fire, there is yin fire. there is (water center)'s fire, there is (earth center)'s fire. there is (metal center)'s fire, there is (wood center)'s fire.

2. 陽火者天上之日月之火。陰火者虛火。此對待之火也。
   yáng huǒ zhě tiānshàng zhī rì yuè zhī huǒ. yīnhuǒ zhě xū huǒ. cǐ duìdài zhī huǒ yě.
   yang fire (is) the sky's sun (and) moon. yin fire is deficient fire. this (is) treatment's fire.

Vocabulary

1.	火	huǒ	fire
2.	中之	zhōng zhī	(noun) within (noun)
	之中	zhī zhōng	in the midst of (noun)
3.	土	tǔ	earth, soil
4.	金	jīn	metal
5.	木	mù	wood
6.	天上	tiān shàng	the sky
	天	tiān	heaven, the sky
	地	dì	earth, the ground

7.	日	rì	day, sun
8.	月	yuè	month, moon
9.	虛	xū	vacuous, deficient
	實	shí	replete, excess
10.	此	cǐ	this, these
	彼	bǐ	that, those
11.	對待	duì dài	to deal with, to treat

Notes

1. 水中之火 contains a grammar pattern that reflects the idea that one item can exist within another. The characters 水中, which are the same as 水之中, mean *in the midst of water* or *within water*. The item following 之, in this case 火, is the smaller part that is within the item before 中. Together, 水中之火 means (*within water*)*'s fire* or *the fire within water*.

Examples:

a. 陰中之陽
yīn zhōng zhī yáng
(within yin)'s yang
the yang within yin

b. 有陽中之陰。
yǒu yáng zhōng zhī yīn.
There is yin within yang.

c. 無上中之下。
wú shàng zhōng zhī xià.
There is no lower within upper.

The characters 之中 are also commonly used to express the existence of one item within another. 之 is possessive in this case, so there will always be a noun before it.

Examples:

a. 陽之中

yáng zhī zhōng

in the midst of yang

within yang

b. 胃之中有水穀。

wèi zhī zhōng yǒu shuǐ gǔ.

In the midst of the stomach there are water and grains.

There are water and grains within the stomach.

c. 日之中火也。

rì zhī zhōng huǒ yě.

Within the sun is fire.

2. In the sentence 陽火者天上之日月之火, the character 之 is used twice and is a possessive marker in each case. 陽火 is clarified as the subject and as a noun with the character 者. The characters 天上之日月 means *the sky's sun and moon*. Looking at the characters 日月之火 together makes it easier to see the meaning of *the sun and moon's fire*. Directly translated, this sentence means *Yang fire (is the) sky's sun (and) moon's fire*. The sun and moon belong to the sky, and this fire belongs to the sun and moon. This is this fire that is being called 陽火. The addition of the 之 after 天上 may be an error by a later editor, as editions both with and without the first 之 exist. For more on when 之 can be omitted, see Chapter Eight, Note 1.

3. 此 means *this*. Sentence two is a good example of how 此 refers to things that are closer, or in this case more recent. In this case, 此 is referring to 陰火者 (*yin fire*). Additionally, common sense must be applied to the interpretation. The author is a physician and would not likely treat the fire of the sun and moon. The character 是 (see Chapter Seven, Note 2) is used in a similar way.

4. The character 也, first introduced in Chapter One, is used for emphasis in the sentence 此對待之火也. The two previous sentences provide a background for the emphasized thought about to be given. This is a common pattern in classical Chinese. The 也 appears in this sentence to emphasize and give finality to the explanation given.

Translation

1. There is yang fire and there is yin fire. There is fire within water, and there is fire within earth. There is fire within metal, and there is fire within wood.

2. Yang-fire is the fire of the sky's sun and moon. Yin-fire is deficiency fire. This is the fire to be treated.

The character 天 means *sky* or *heavens* and contains a pictograph of a person with outstretched arms (大) below and a cover above (一). Some try to make this character fit modern spiritual notions, while others wish to take all spiritual connotations out of 天 and translate it only as *sky*. Sticking to one side or another is too limited, as this character is used to represent both the literal sky above and the more abstract concept of something above (or beyond the control) of humans. This depends greatly on the time period, the context of the character within a specific text, and the background of the author. The meaning of this character can even differ within different sentences of the same text. Remain open to the context of the text and interpreting this character will be simple.

Unit Two

Chapter Five

藏各有一耳腎獨有兩者
何也然腎兩者非皆腎也
其左者為腎右者為命門
故男子以藏精女子以繫
胞故知腎有一也

1. 藏各有一耳。腎獨有兩者何也？
zàng gè yǒu yī ěr. shèn dú yǒu liǎngzhě hé yě?

2. 然。腎兩者非皆腎也。其左者爲腎右者爲命門。
rán. shèn liǎng zhě fēi jiē shèn yě. qí zuǒ zhě wéi shèn, yòu zhě wéi mìng mén.

3. 故男子以藏精，女子以繫胞。故知腎有一也
gù nán zi yǐ cáng jīng, nǚ zi yǐ jì bāo. gù zhī shèn yǒu yī yě.

Vocabulary

1.	藏	zàng	zang organ, depot (also written as 臟)
2.	各	gè	each, every
3.	耳	ěr	short for 而已
	而已	éryǐ	only, that's all, then stop
4.	獨有	dú yǒu	alone has
5.	何	hé	how/what; a question word
6.	何也	hé yě	How is it that...?; Why?
7.	然	rán	(to be) like this
8.	非	fēi	not; It's not true that...
9.	皆	jiē	all, every, both
10.	其	qí	his, her, its, their

11.	左	zuǒ	left
	左者	zuǒzhě	the left one
12.	爲	wéi	to serve as, is considered
13.	右	yòu	right
	右者	yòuzhě	the right one
14.	故	gù	therefore, hence, so reason
15.	男子	nán zi	a male, males
	男	nán	male
	子	zǐ	son, seed, person
16.	以	yǐ	so as to (verb) uses (noun)
17.	藏	cáng	to store
18.	精	jīng	essence
19.	女子	nǚ zi	a female, females
20.	繫	jì	to tie, to bind
21.	胞	bāo	uterus
22.	知	zhī	to know

Notes

1. 耳 represents the characters 而已 (ér yǐ), which are used as a final particle meaning *only* or *that's all.* This compound literally means *then stop*. Final particles are important to recognize because they help readers identify the end of a thought or sentence. They take the place of punctuation, of which the original classics had none. So far, 也 (yě), 焉 (yān) and 耳 (ěr) have been covered.

2. 獨 is followed by helping verbs such as 有 or 能 (néng) to emphasize that the subject alone can complete the action. Here, 腎獨有 means *the kidney alone has*. For a comparison of 獨 with other characters that have similar meanings and functions, see Chapter Nine, Note one.

3. 何 is a general question word that can mean *why, how* or *what*. The placement of this character within a sentence can vary greatly. 何 can be placed before or after a verb and usually occurs after the noun it is asking about.

Examples:

a. 其病，治之何？
qí bìng, zhì zhī hé?
How is his disease to be treated?
His disease, treat it how?

b. 陰下陽何？
yīn xià yáng hé?
How does yin descend yang?

c. 從道何？
cóng dào hé?
How is the Way followed?

The compound 何也 is more common in medical texts than the above grammar pattern. These two characters are asking for more information about the previous clause. In the question and answer format of the 難經 (nán jīng), these two characters are the preferred way to ask questions.

Examples:

a. 醫之治病，何也?

yī zhī zhì bìng, hé yě?

How is it that physicians treat disease?

Physicians treat disease. How is this so?

b. 腎有兩岐，何也?

shèn yǒu liǎng qí, hé yě?

Why does the kidney have two branches?

How is it that the kidney has two branches?

4. 然 means *It's like this.* Seeing this character indicates that an explanation will follow when a question immediately precedes it. Where 何也 marks the request for an explanation, 然 follows it to show that a new person is speaking and about to offer that explanation. 然 appears in every chapter of the 難經.

5. 非 negates nouns, concepts, or ideas. The characters placed between 非 and 也 (when it appears) are the characters being negated. In this chapter, 非 negates 皆腎, *both kidneys.* The sentence 腎兩者非皆腎也 can therefore be interpreted as follows: *The two kidneys are not both kidneys.* The character 非 can also negate ideas, so the sentence 非腎兩者皆腎也 would be interpreted as: *It is not the case that the two are both kidneys.*

Examples:

a. 非心水穀之道路也。

fēi xīn shuǐ gǔ zhī dào lù yě.

It is not the case that the heart is the path of the water and grains.

b. 心非水穀之道路也。

xīn fēi shuǐ gǔ zhī dào lù yě.

The heart is not the path of the water and grains.

c. 非腎也，命門也。

fēi shèn yě, mìng mén yě.

It is not the kidney, it is the life gate.

6. 其 is a possessive pronoun that can mean *his*, *her*, *their*, or *its* in English. This character is confusing for beginners, as it does not make distinctions between people or things. 其左者 means *its left one*, with the *it* referring to *the two kidneys*. This sentence could also be written in classical Chinese as 腎兩者之左者 or *(the two kidney)'s left one*. In both English and classical Chinese, the subject would not be repeated. An English author would use *its* and a classical Chinese author would use 其.

Examples:

a. 醫治其病。

yī zhì qí bìng.

The physician treated her illness.

b. 其肝無血。

qí gān wú xuè.

His liver has no blood.

c. 女子有胞。其腎主之。

nǚ zi yǒu bāo. qí shèn zhǔ zhī.

Females have a uterus. Their kidneys govern it.

7. 故 can be used at the beginning of a sentence as a marker that begins an explanation of a previous statement or adds to previous information. The most basic meaning of this character is *reason*. When used at the beginning of a sentence, however, it means *therefore* or *moreover*. In this chapter, the character's two appearances needed two different translations.

8. 以 alone has no meaning. One must refer to the surrounding words and context to understand it. Use these basic formulas for interpretation:

When 以 is followed by a verb, it means *so as to*.
Example:
a. 心主血以下陽。
xīn zhǔ xuè yǐ xià yáng.
The heart rules the blood so as to descend yang.

b. 腎主骨以繫身。
shèn zhǔ gǔ yǐ jì shēn.
The kidney rules the bones so as to bind the body.

When 以 is followed by a noun, it means *by means of* or *with*. The noun is used to complete the action of the verb. The 以 + *noun* structure may appear before or after the verb, each producing a slightly different effect.
Example:
a. 陰以血下陽。
yīn yǐ xuè xià yáng.
Yin descends yang with blood.

b. 陰下陽以血。
yīn xià yáng yǐ xuè.
It is with blood that yin descends yang.

The sentence 男子以藏精 is even trickier than the above examples. Here, 以 is followed by the character 藏, which can be either a verb (cáng, *to store*) or a noun (zàng, *zang organ*). Because 以 can be followed by both nouns and verbs, this sentence requires more work to interpret. When encountering this problem, work out the possible meanings to see what makes sense. Treating 藏 as a verb, this sentence would mean *Men so as to store essence*. This is obviously awkward. Looking at 藏 as a noun would leave the interpretation *Men store the essence by means of the zang organs*. This makes no sense, given the context.

Neither of these possibilities fit because the noun following 以 may be omitted if the context is clear. The author omitted the noun that should follow 以 because he assumed the reader would know he is talking about the 命門, which was the last subject discussed. This sentence could have been written as 男子以命門藏精, or *Men store essence by means of the life gate*. One might think that 之 could or should be used as a pronoun in the following way: 男子以之藏精. This is never the case, however, as authors omit the noun after 以 when it is the subject of the last sentence or the chapter. The same usage is applied in the next part of this sentence: *Women bind the uterus by means of the life gate*.

Translation

Each zang has only one (entity). The kidney alone has two. Why is this so? It's like this. The two entities of the kidney are not both kidneys. Its left one is considered the kidney. Its right one is considered the life gate. Moreover, in men it stores the essence, (and) in women it binds the uterus. Therefore, one knows the kidney has one (entity).

藏

This character contains a grass radical at the top. (a modified 艸) The lower portion contains 臧 , which represents goods stored for long term use. This character is referring to long term storage *under the grass*, or within a deep space. Physicians first borrowed this character to refer to the group of organs that store the influences necessary for survival. When referring to the organs, later writers use the character 臟 , which includes the flesh radical (a modified 月). This character represents a long-term storage area within the body. In earlier texts, however, this distinction was not made. Therefore, there are many texts where this character is used to represent two completely different meanings within the same sentence.

Chapter Six

難經二十五曰有十二經五藏六府十一耳其一經者何等經也然一經者手少陰與心主別脈也心主與三焦為表裏具有名而無形故言經有十二也

1. 難經二十五曰：有十二經，五藏，六府，十一耳。其一經者何等經也？
   nán jīng èrshíwǔ yuē: yǒu shíèr jīng, wǔ zàng, liù fǔ, shíyī ěr. qí yī jīng zhě hé děng jīng yě?

2. 然。一經者手少陰與心主別脈也。心主與三焦爲表裏。
   rán. yī jīng zhě shǒushǎoyīn yǔ xīn zhǔ bié mài yě. xīn zhǔ yǔ sān jiāo wéi biǎo lǐ.

3. 具有名而無形。故言經有十二也。
   jù yǒu míng ér wú xíng. gù yán jīng yǒu shíèr yě.

Vocabulary

1.	難經	nán jīng	*The Classic of Difficulties*
2.	二十五	èrshíwǔ	twenty-five
3.	曰	yuē *	to say (quote), speak of, to call
4.	十二	shíèr	twelve
	十一	shíyī	eleven
5.	經	jīng	meridian, channel, vessel classic
6.	府	fǔ	fu organ, palace (腑)
	小腸	xiǎo cháng	small intestine
	大腸	dà cháng	large intestine
	胃	wèi	stomach
	膀胱	pang guāng	urinary bladder

	膽	dǎn	gallbladder
7.	何等	hé děng	what kind of, what else
	等	děng	class, ranking, group
8.	手少陰	shǒushǎoyīn	hand minor-yin
	手	shǒu	hand
	足	zú	foot
	少	shǎo	minor, lesser, few
	多	duō	great, more, many
9.	心主	xīn zhǔ	heart master, pericardium (*sic*)
10.	脈	mài, mò	vessel, pulse position
11.	具有	jùyǒu	to possess, to have, to provide
	具	jù	a tool; fully, completely
12.	而	ér	then, and, but; and yet
13.	無形	wú xíng	formless, without form
	形	xíng	form, shape
14.	故言	gù yán	therefore it is said
	言	yán	words, speech
			to talk about, to say, to speak

Notes

1. Counting the numbers one through 10 is easy, as they have just one character each. Counting numbers between 11 and 99 becomes more difficult. Use the guide below to better understand how these numbers are counted.

11: 十一	shí yī	18: 十八	shí bā
23: 二十三	èr shí sān	56: 五十六	wǔ shí liù
77: 七十七	qī shí qī	81: 八十一	bā shí yī
94: 九十四	jiǔ shí sì		

2. 曰 and 言 have essentially the same meaning, but their usage differs. First, 曰 can introduce a quote from a book or a person. Although the phrase following 曰 is usually a direct quote, it may be a summary instead of the exact words used in a text. In addition, if 曰 precedes a name, then that person *is called* the name that follows rather than being quoted.

Where 曰 typically indicates a direct quote, 言 points toward a generalization based on another text or statement. In this passage, 故言 means *therefore it is said.* The characters following 故言 are a summary of an idea and there is no identifiable person being quoted. In the examples below, (a) could stand by itself, while (b) is a conclusion based on something previously stated.

Examples:

a. 內經曰心主血。

nèi jīng yuē xīn zhǔ xuè.

The *Inner Classic* says the heart rules blood.

b. 故言心主血。
gù yán xīn zhǔ xuè.
Therefore it is said the heart rules blood.

3. The character 曰 (to say, yuē) looks very similar to the previously covered character 日 (the sun, rì). The former is wider than the latter. Modern typefaces allow readers to see the differences between these characters more easily. In the original Chinese writing, the differences between these two characters may be more difficult to discern depending on the type of printing used.

4. 其一經者 is a complicated phrase. First, ascertain what 其 (*his*, *her*, or *its*) refers to. In this passage, the author uses 其 to mean *its*, which refers to the body. In classical Chinese, authors can refer back to items that are implied but not directly stated. The questioner has stated there are twelve meridians, five *zang* organs, and six *fu* organs. There is one extra meridian, which is what the question is about. The body contains all of these and the author is making an assumption that readers know this. The word *its* cannot be used this way in English, as it must refer back to something previously stated.

The character 者 makes 一經 (one meridian) a noun while also emphasizing this is the subject of the sentence. The one meridian being referred to is the "extra one" that cannot be accounted for among the eleven related to the *zang* and *fu* organs. Taken alone, this phrase means *its one meridian* or *this one meridian*.

5. 何等 , like 何也, requests more information. The character 等 means *group* or *class*. 何, being a general question word, is asking about how to group this unclassified meridian. The difference between 何等 and 何也 is that rather than asking for more information about a previous clause, 何等 asks about the group to which something belongs so that it can be further classified and understood.

6. 一經者手少陰與心主別脈也 This sentence was preceded by 然, which indicates that an answer is coming. The first sentence in the answer to this question needs to be analyzed in smaller parts to be understood. Commentators have debated the meaning and implications of this answer for centuries. This line is a great example of how learning to read the classics does not mean that one will be able to come up with a concrete understanding of every passage.

一經者 follows the pattern explained above. The character 者 marks 一經 as the subject while also clarifying that these two characters are a noun compound. As mentioned before, the final particle 也 (yě) serves to finalize the answer. This sentence can be broken down to make the meaning clearer:

一經者	yī jīng zhě	the one meridian (noun-subject)
手少陰	shǒu shǎo yīn	hand minor-yin (heart)
與	yǔ	gives (or *with*; *to accompany*)
心主	xīn zhǔ	the heart master
別脈	bié mà	distinct (but related) vessel
也	yě	end particle

First, the meaning of 別脈 needs to be looked at closely. This is the only time these two characters are used together in the 難經, so we must look outside of it for help. While this can be rendered into English as *distinct* or *different vessel*, this does not mean that it is completely separate. The 外經 (wài jīng) states that the extraordinary vessel known as 陰蹻脈 (yin motility or yin heel vessel, yīn qiāo mài) is a 別脈 of foot minor-yin (kidney). Chinese medicine students will remember learning that this vessel internally links with, and can be accessed through, the kidney meridian; therefore, these two meridians are distinct (別) but not without a relationship.

Second, the term for the meridian of the 心主 is not treated the same as other meridians in the 難經. The term 手厥陰 (hand ceasing-yin, shǒu jué yīn) never occurs in the 難經. In fact, Case 24 states 厥陰者肝脈也 (ceasing-yin is the liver meridian, jué yīn zhě gān mài yě). Throughout the text, the heart master vessel is referred to as 手心主 (hand heart master, shǒu xīn zhǔ) and is the only vessel not given its own yin or yang correspondence. It is important to point out that 心主 refers to an entity through which the heart rules rather than an entity that rules the heart. In these early texts, it is in no way referring to what modern medicine refers to as the pericardium (see note 8 below).

Finally, the character 與 (yǔ) has many meanings. As in Chapter Three, it can be used as a conjunction meaning *with* or *together with*. As a verb, it most often means *to give*, but at times it can also mean *to accompany*. The explanation below will first assume 與 was used as a verb meaning *to give*, and later tests the possibility that it was used as a conjunction meaning *with* or the verb meaning *to accompany*.

The interpretation of 與 meaning *to give* makes the most sense in this case. In English, this can be translated as *(This) one meridian is (the result of) hand minor-yin bestowing the heart master (with a) distinct meridian.* The heart is the ruler in ancient physiology and would bestow upon other meridians their functions. This reading most closely follows the analysis above.

Yet another reasonable interpretation would be to read 與 as the conjunction *with.* In this case, the emphasis changes only slightly. This could be translated as *(This) one meridian is a distinct vessel (of) hand minor-yin and the heart master.* Finally, if 與 is taken as the verb *to accompany,* this sentence means *(This) one meridian is (a result of) hand minor-yin accompanying the heart master.* This is more likely to be favored if the *heart master* is seen as a branch of the heart meridian, or *hand minor-yin.*

Based on all of this analysis, it can be said that within the 難經, this one vessel is given the name *hand heart master.* It is not 手厥陰 (shǒu jué yīn), which does not exist at this point. It is distinct from, but has a close relationship with the hand minor-yin (heart) vessel. It cannot be said concretely that this vessel is a branch of hand minor-yin, though this would be a reasonable interpretation. While this answer raised as many questions as it answered, it is clear that modern Chinese medicine has changed the way it looks at this meridian.

7. 而 is a conjunction that can mean *and*, *but*, or *then* depending on the context. This character connects two or more verbs (or verb phrases) within a sentence, which is how it is distinct from other characters that also mean *then*.

Examples:

a. 醫從陰陽而治其 病。

yī cóng yīn yáng ér zhì qí bìng.

The physician followed yin yang and treated her disease.

b. 肺主皮而身生焉。

fèi zhǔ pí ér shēn shēng yān.

The lung rules the skin, and the body is generated within it.

8. 有...而無... This pattern makes a distinction about the subject being discussed—the subject has something, but is lacking something else. The noun following 有 is possessed by the subject; the noun following 無 is not. In this passage 有名而無形 means that the heart master and triple warmer *have a name, but no form.* This is yet another reason why the interpretation of 心主 as pericardium is not accurate. The pericardium has a form and refers to the outer membrane surrounding the heart. 心主 is pointing to something else entirely.

Translation

Nanjing Chapter 25 states: There are twelve meridians, five *zang* organs and six *fu* organs totaling only eleven. What type of meridian is this one (extra) meridian? It's like this. This one (extra) meridian is (the result of) hand minor-yin bestowing the heart master (with a) distinct meridian. The heart master and triple burner are considered interior and exterior (in relationship). (They) possess a name, but have no form. Therefore, it is said there are twelve meridians.

On the left is the radical 糸, which represents fine threads twisted together. On the right appears 巠, showing an underground river with a person underneath. This character has many meanings, all of which are common in medical texts. 經 is used to denote respected written works in many types of Chinese literature, including religion, philosophy and medicine. It also means *meridian* or *vessel*, as in the compound 經脈 (jīng mài).

Chapter Seven

五藏所藏心藏神肺藏魄肝藏魂
脾藏意腎藏志是謂五藏所藏五
藏所主心主脈肺主皮肝主筋脾
主肉腎主骨是謂五主五勞所傷
久視傷血久臥傷氣久坐傷肉久
立傷骨久行傷筋是謂五勞所傷
五脈應象肝脈絃心脈鉤脾脈代
肺脈毛腎脈石是謂五藏之脈

1. 五藏所藏：心藏神，肺藏魄，肝藏魂，脾藏意，腎藏志。是謂五藏所藏。
   wǔ zàng suǒ cáng: xīn cáng shén, fèi cáng pò, gān cáng hún, pí cáng yì, shèn cáng zhì. shì wèi wǔ zàng suǒ cáng.
2. 五藏所主：心主脈，肺主皮，肝主筋，脾主肉，腎主骨。是謂五主。
   wǔ zàng suǒ zhǔ: xīn zhǔ mài, fèi zhǔ pí, gān zhǔ jīn, pí zhǔ ròu, shèn zhǔ gǔ. shì wèi wǔ zhǔ.
3. 五勞所傷：久視傷血，久臥傷氣，久坐傷肉，久立傷骨，久行傷筋。是謂五勞所傷。
   wǔ láo suǒ shāng: jiǔ shì shāng xuè, jiǔ wò shāng qì, jiǔ zuò shāng ròu, jiǔ lì shāng gǔ, jiǔ xíng shāng jié. shì wèi wǔ láo suǒ shāng.
4. 五脈應象：肝脈絃，心脈鉤，脾脈代，肺脈毛，腎脈石·是謂五藏之脈。
   wǔ mài yìng xiàng: gān mài xián, xīn mài gōu, pí mài dài,fèi mài máo, shèn mài shí. shì wèi wǔ zàng zhī mài.

Vocabulary

1.	所	suǒ	that which is, what is
2.	神	shén	spirit, mind, a god
3.	魄	pò	the animalistic soul
4.	魂	hún	the human soul
5.	意	yì	thought, wisdom, intention
6.	志	zhì	will, willpower

7.	是謂	shì wèi	this is called, this is known as
8.	是	shì	this
9.	謂	wèi	to be called, to say or state
10.	筋	jīn	tendons
11.	肉	ròu	flesh, muscles
12.	勞	láo	work, labor, fatigue
13.	傷	shāng	to injur, damage
14.	久	jiǔ	long time, long term, lasting
15.	視	shì	to look at, to inspect
16.	臥	wò	to sleep
17.	坐	zuò	to sit
18.	立	lì	to stand
19.	行	xíng	to walk, to move about
20.	應	yīng	to correspond
21.	象	xiàng	reflection, appearance, image
22.	絃	xián	wiry, string-like
23.	鉤	gōu	hook-like
24.	代	dài	intermittent

25. 毛 máo thin, hair-like

26. 石 shí stone-like, rolling

Notes

1. 所 changes the verb that follows it into an object and when used in this way means *that which*. Compare the following examples to see how 所 changes the meaning of a group of characters.

Examples:

a. 所治

suǒ zhì

that which is treated

醫所治病也。

yī suǒ zhì bìng yě.

That which doctors treat is disease.

醫之治病也。

yī zhī zhì bìng yě.

Doctors treat disease.

b. 所傷

suǒ shāng

that which is injured

久坐所傷肉也。

jiǔ zuò suǒ shāng ròu yě.

That which long-term sitting injures is the muscles.

久坐傷肉。

jiǔ zuò shāng ròu.

Long-term sitting injures muscles.

c. 所主
suǒ zhǔ
that which is ruled
心所主非骨也。
xīn suǒ zhǔ fēi gǔ yě.
That which the heart rules is not the bones.
心不主骨。
xīn bù zhǔ gǔ.
The heart does not rule the bones.
(for more on 不, see Chapter Eleven, note 4)

2. 是 means *this* and refers back to a subject that was mentioned in a recent sentence—usually the sentence preceding it. Sometimes in classical Chinese, this is done with different characters (彼 and 此, see Chapter Four, Note 3). The use of *this* and *that* usually relies on distance of the object from the subject— *this* is close, while *that* is far. The character 是 does not make such a distinction, but it can be safely assumed that it means *this* in most cases, as it usually refers to a recently mentioned subject.

3. When 是 and 謂 are combined, they mean *this is called.* The author uses this phrase to give a name to the last topic discussed. In English, *this is referred to as* or *this is called* matches the meaning of this phrase.

4. 久 is used to refer to a long period of time. A noun, verb, or even a situation can follow it. For example, the sentence 久病則死 directly translated means *If for a long time illness then dead.* To put this simple four-character phrase into more understandable English, we could say *If one is ill for a long time, then (that person) will die.*

5. The character 應 means *to correspond* and 象 is an *image* or *appearance*. Together, the characters 應象 mean *corresponding image*. The pulse *correspondences* refer to the organs of that pulse, while the *images* or *impressions* are a description of what the practitioner will feel when palpating the pulse.

6. Notice that in the last section of this chapter, the five phrases beginning with 肝脈絃 are missing the character 也 at the end. When there is a list being written, this character is usually omitted. In addition, because earlier statements such as 心藏神 contain a verb (in this case 藏, cáng), the author would not add 也 unless he wished to conclude a series of statements with a strong emphasis.

Translation

That which the zang organs store (are as follows): the heart stores the spirit; the lung stores the animal spirit; the liver stores the human spirit; the spleen stores thought; the kidney stores will. This is called that which the five zang store.

That which the five zang organs rule (are as follows): the heart rules the vessels; the lung rules the skin; the liver rules the tendons; the spleen rules the muscles; the kidney rules the bones. These are called the five rulers.

That which the five labors injure (are as follows): long-term looking injures blood; long-term sleeping damages the qi; long-term sitting damages the muscles; long-term standing damages the bones; long-term walking damages the tendons. This is called that which the five labors injure.

The five corresponding images of the pulse are as follows: the liver pulse is wiry; the heart pulse is hook-like; the spleen pulse is intermittent; the lung pulse is thin; the kidney pulse is stone-like. These are called the pulses of the five zang organs.

This character uses the radical 示. According to some interpretations, this character is a modified 三 which represents the three celestial aspects: sun, moon, and stars. In other interpretations, it is something finer than the silk radical (糸), as 示 contains one stroke less stroke than silk. In this interpretation, 示 is something so fine it is indiscernible to the human eye. The right side, in its earliest meanings, is *spirit*. It can also be a verb meaning to extend. This character can refer to a god or to the finest spiritual matter of a human being.

Chapter Eight

人面獨能耐寒者何也然人頭者諸陽之會也諸陰脈皆至頸胸中而還獨諸陽脈皆上至頭耳故令面耐寒也

1. 人面獨能耐寒者何也? 然。人頭者諸陽之會也。
   rén miàn dú néng nài hán zhě hé yě. rán. rén tóu zhě zhū yáng zhī huì yě.

2. 諸陰脈皆至頸胸中而還。獨諸陽脈皆上至頭耳。故令面耐寒也。
   zhū yīn mài jiē zhì jǐng xiōng zhōng ér huán. dú zhū yáng mài jiē shàng zhì tóu ěr. gù lìng miàn nài hán yě.

Vocabulary

1.	人	rén	people, person, human
2.	面	miàn	face
3.	人面	rén miàn	people's faces
4.	能	néng	able, can be, can
	獨能	dú néng	alone can
5.	耐	nài	to stand, to bear, to endure
6.	寒	hán	cold
	寒者	hánzhě	the cold, cold things
7.	頭	tóu	head
8.	諸	zhū	many, all, each, various the class or group of
9.	會	huì	meeting place, assembly

10. 至	zhì	to (a place), arrive
11. 頸	jǐng, gěng	neck
12. 胸	xiōng	chest
13. 中	zhōng	within, in the center of
14. 還	huán	to return (a thing or to a place)
15. 上至	shàng zhì	rises to, go up to
16. 令	lìng	to cause, to make, to order also written as 令

Notes

1. 人面 means *people's faces*, but is not written with a possessive marker (人之面) to indicate the possessive as the English does. In this case, classical Chinese does not use the possessive because the object is inseparable from the person and therefore cannot be possessed. This also occurs in the next sentence with 人頭. This rule extends into other relationships, including country, family members, emperor, and spouse, among others.

Examples:

a. 女頸
nǚ jǐng
women's necks

b. 男胸
nán xiōng
men's chests

c. 人身
rén shēn
people's bodies

d. 天上日月
tiānshàng rìyuè
the sun and moon of the sky

2. 者 usually refers to the characters nearest to it. The first use of this character occurs in the question 人面獨能耐寒者何也. The meaning of 何也 is explained in Chapter Five, Note Three. Working "backwards," or in the case of Classical Chinese, upwards, from 者 is the best technique to discover this character's meaning.

First, 寒 is an adjective meaning *cold*, and the author could make it a noun by adding 者. This means *the cold* and in the context of this sentence would mean *people's faces alone can bear* ***the cold***. This makes sense, so it can be set aside as a possibility.

者 could also be read as 耐寒者, meaning *those who bear cold*. If this meaning were to be included in the rest of the sentence's translation, the overall meaning would be *people's faces alone can* ***those who bear cold***. This does not make sense and can be excluded as a possibility.

This character can also help to make the subject clear. 人面 prominently stands out as the subject. The character 者 comes after 耐, which is the main verb of the sentence. The character 者 would never be added after the verb to make 人面 stand out as the subject, so we can eliminate this meaning.

In this sentence, the first meaning is the only possible interpretation of this character. A major function of this character is to *nominalize*, or turn something into a noun which is not a noun. If one knows that the adjective *cold* has been turned into a noun, then the basic meaning of *things that are cold* or *the cold* is easy to infer.

In the second sentence of line one, 者 helps to identify 人頭 as the subject by immediately following it. In the previous sentence, 者 was used to turn 寒 into a noun and could not be used in the same sentence to also make the subject clear. The sentence 人面者獨能耐寒者 would be repetitive for classical Chinese writers. After 人頭者 comes 諸陽之會也, which means *the meeting place of all yang (vessels)*. This is similar to the AB 也 formula learned in Chapter One. A 者 B 也 uses 者 to simply help separate A and B within that formula—A is a noun-subject and B is either another noun or a phrase. To make this into a negative statement, the character 非 (fēi) can be used: A 者 非 B 也.

Examples:

a. 人胸者非諸陰之會也。
   rén xiōng zhě fēi zhū yīn zhī huì yě.
   People's chests are not the meeting place of yin.

b. 人身者生死之門也。
   rén shēn zhě shēng sǐ zhī mén yě.
   People's bodies are the gate of life and death.

c. 病者人身之命也。
   bìngzhě rén shēn zhī mìng yě.
   Illness is the fate of human's bodies.

3. 諸 can mean either *all* or *group*. The terms 諸陽 and 諸陰 are commonly seen together when discussing meridians or organs that belong to the 陰陽 categories. This character is similar to 等 (děng), but is used differently. The term 諸陰 refers to all of the items that belong in the 陰 category. 等 陰 would refer to the category of 陰 itself. Therefore, 諸陰之會, meaning *the gathering place of all yin* makes sense, but 等陰

之會 would not make sense because it does not contain the inherent meaning of *all*.

4. 令 The meaning of this character is *to allow* or *to make*. In the sentence above, 令面耐寒 means *allows the face to bear cold*. The character after 令, in this case 面, is usually present as the object *made* or *allowed* to complete the following action. At times, however, the object can be left out. In such cases, 令 can be thought of as *to allow for*. In a similar manner, this English phrase does not require an object. This sentence could have been written as 故令耐寒也 if the author had thought that 面 was obviously the object.

Examples:

a. 令其血欝
lìng qí xuè yù
allows his blood (to become) depressed

b. 令其身寒
lìng qí shēn hán
allows her body (to become) cold

c. 令人身有病焉
lìng rén shēn yǒu bìng yān.
makes the body have an illness within *or*
let the body have an illness within (a command)

Translation

How is it that people's faces are alone able to bear cold? It's like this: the head is the meeting place of all yang (vessels). The yin vessels all arrive at the neck (or) center of the chest and then return. The yang vessels alone all rise to the head. Therefore, (this) allows the face to bear cold.

This character represents a roofed structure with people underneath packing hay for warmth. The title of the classic text, 傷寒論 (shāng hán lùn), uses this character. This selection from the 難經 focused on one aspect of how the Chinese viewed the human body's interaction with cold. One of the earliest discussions in Chinese medicine, which continues up to today, was how the human body, with its various excesses and deficiencies, interact with cold to either create or resist disease.

Chapter Nine

藏唯有五府獨有六者何也然所以府有六者謂三焦也有原氣之別焉主持諸氣有名而無形其經屬手少陽此外府也故言府有六焉

1. 藏唯有五。府獨有六者何也？
   zàng wéi yǒu wǔ. fǔ dú yǒu liù zhě hé yě?

2. 然。所以府有六者謂三焦也。有原氣之別焉。主持諸氣。
   rán. suǒ yǐ fǔ yǒu liù zhě wèi sān jiāo yě. yǒu yuán qì zhī bié yān. zhǔ chí zhū qì.

3. 有名而無形。其經屬手少陽。此外府也。故言府有六焉。
   yǒu míng ér wú xíng. qí jīng shǔ shǒu shǎo yáng. cì wài fǔ yě. gù yán fǔ yǒu liù yān.

Vocabulary

1.	唯有	wéi yǒu	only have, only has
	唯	wéi	only
2.	所以	suǒ yǐ	that by which
3.	原氣	yuán qì	original qi, source qi
4.	主持	zhǔ chí	to manage, to lead
5.	氣	qì	qi, vapor, function, breath
6.	屬	shǔ	to belong to (a category)
7.	外	wài	outside, outer
	內	nèi	inside, inner

Notes

1. 唯 means *only* and may be followed by any type of verb, a noun or even a sentence to modify the entire sentence. This book has already covered other characters with the general meaning of *only*. For example, 獨 means *alone* and is usually followed by a helping verb such as 有 or 能. Sentence one provides a chance to examine the difference between 唯 and 獨 more closely. The phrase 藏唯有五 points out that the *zang* organs number **only** five, emphasizing their relative lack. However, the sentence 府獨有六 points out that the *fu* organs **alone** total six. This difference is quite subtle.

The character 耳 is similar to 唯 in that it also means *only* and can modify the entire clause. When modifying an entire clause, however, 唯 is placed at the beginning of the sentence while 耳 is placed at the end. Both 唯 and 獨 can be found in combination with 耳 when authors want to create a strong emphasis for *only*.

Examples:

a. 府獨有六耳。
 fǔ dúyǒu liù ěr.
 The Fu organs alone have six!

b. 唯醫治病耳。
 wéi yī zhì bìng ěr.
 Only physicians treat disease!

c. 肝唯藏魂耳。
 gān wéi cáng hún ěr.
 Only the liver stores the human soul!

2. The characters 所以 combine to change the emphasis of a sentence and the verb that follows it. As seen before, 所 changes a verb into an object (see Chapter Seven, Note 1). The character 以 was covered in Chapter Five, Note 8. The characters 所以 mean *the means by which* and in most cases are directly followed by a verb. In the passage above, the sentence reads 所以府有 or *the means by which the fu organs have*. This is because 有 is a helping verb and would not immediately follow 所以. If the verb of the sentence is an action verb, then the verb immediately follows 所以, while the subject is placed in front of it.

Examples:

a. 陰所以下陽血也。
yīn suǒyǐ xià yáng xuè yě.
The means by which yin descends yang is blood.

b. 男子所以藏精命門也。
nánzǐ suǒyǐ cáng jīng mìngmén yě.
The means by which men store essence is the life gate.

c. 人所以藏神心也。
rén suǒyǐ cáng shén xīn yě.
The means by which humans store the spirit is the heart.

3. 所以府有六者謂三焦也 First, be careful with the three characters 有六者. These characters should **not** be read together with the pattern learned in Chapter Three, Note one as *there are those who (that) are six*. This sentence becomes much easier when it is broken down as follows:

所以府有	The means by which the fu have
六者	six (made into a noun)
謂三焦	is called the triple warmer
也	(end particle)

The phrase 所以府有 needs to be read together as explained above in Note 2. The character 六 is made into a noun by 者. If the phrase would have read 府有六, this would mean *the fu organs have the number six*. The addition of 者 allows the number six to become a noun, which becomes *six entities*. The verb 謂 is used here to give a name to that which allows the *fu* organs to have six entities.

4. This chapter contains the full text of Case 38 of the 難經. The simplicity allows the reader the chance to review many of the characters taught up to this point. Even though this passage contains at total of 53 characters, there are only a few new words. If you thought this chapter was easy, then you have studied the previous chapters well. If you struggled with this chapter, review the previous chapters again. Throughout medical literature, the characters and grammar appearing up to this point appear repeatedly. Memorizing the characters in this book and understanding the grammar is essential for reading medical texts.

Translation

How is it that there are only five *zang* organs (and) the *fu* alone have six? It's like this: The triple warmer is named as (the reason) the *fu* have six entities. (It) has the difference of original qi within it (and) manages qi. It has a name but no form. Its meridian belongs to (the category of) hand minor-yang. This is an external *fu*. Therefore, it is said that there are six fu.

Much discussion and debate surround this character. Inside is 米, which is a single grain of rice, or one small part of a whole. The outer portion, 气, is arguably either a pictograph of clouds or a pot. The meaning of this character alone is difficult to discuss, as its true meaning comes out when combined with other characters with meanings ranging from *anger* to *climate* to *breath*. All combinations which include this character are phenomena which are not necessarily visible to the human eye directly, but might be seen or sensed through other means.

Chapter Ten

黃帝問於岐伯鬱之甚者治之奈何岐伯曰木鬱達之火鬱發之土鬱奪之金鬱泄之水鬱折之然調其氣

1. 黃帝問於岐伯: 鬱之甚者，治之奈何? 岐伯曰:
   huángdì wèn yú qíbó: yù zhī shènzhě, zhì zhī nàihé? qíbó yuē:
2. 木鬱達之。火鬱發之。土鬱奪之。金鬱泄之。水鬱折之。然，調其氣。
   mù yù dá zhī. huǒ yù fā zhī. tǔ yù duó zhī. jīn yù xiè zhī. shuǐ yù zhé zhī. rán, tiáo qí qì.

Vocabulary

1.	黃帝	huángdì	Yellow Emperor
2.	問	wèn	to ask
3.	問於	wèn yú	to ask a question to (person)
4.	岐伯	Qí Bó	one of the emperor's teachers
5.	鬱	yù	depressed deficient and stagnant
6.	甚	shèn	extreme, extremely
7.	奈何	nài hé	Why? How? For what reason?
8.	達	dá	to outthrust
9.	發	fā	to effuse, to release
10.	奪	duó	to strip away, to take by force
11.	泄	xiè	to disperse, to drain

12. 折 zhé to break

13. 調 tiáo to regulate

Notes

1. 黃帝問於岐伯 in direct translation reads *The Yellow Emperor asked to Qi Bo*. Sometimes, the character 曰 (yuē) is added in this way: 黃帝問於岐伯曰 meaning *The Yellow Emperor asked Qi Bo saying*. The addition of this character does not change the meaning of this sentence—the emperor is still asking the question. This combination is common in the 內經 (nèi jīng), as it helps to clarify which of the emperor's teachers is being asked a question.

Examples:

a. 帝問於岐伯曰, 治其火奈何？
dì wèn yú Qí Bó yuē, zhì qí huǒ nài hé?
The emperor asked Qi Bo, "How is his fire to be treated?"
岐伯曰, 有火則發之。
Qí Bó yuē, yǒu huǒ zé fā zhī.
Qi Bo said, "If there is fire, then effuse it."

b. 黃蒂問於崎伯, 主心何等經也?
Huáng Dì wèn yú Qí Bó, zhǔ xīn hé děng jīng yě?
The Yellow Emperor asked Qi Bo, "What type of meridian is the heart master?"
崎伯曰:主心與手少陰別脈。
Qí Bó yuē: zhǔxīn yǔ shǒushǎoyīn bié mài.
Qi Bo said, "The Heart Master is a distinct branch of hand minor-yin."

2. 於 was covered in Chapter Two as part of 焉, which is short for 於之 (*in it*). This is the most basic preposition in Chinese and its uses vary so much that its exact meaning can be difficult to decipher. 於 gives direction to the verbs it follows and most often means *to* or *by*.

Outside of medical texts, 問於 usually means *asked by*. In the 內經, the Yellow Emperor is clearly asking questions because his teachers are clearly answering (崎伯曰). In other words, 問於 can have two opposite possible meanings which can only be distinguished by reading an entire text in context. Another use of 於 is outlined in Chapter Thirteen, Note 3.

3. 鬱之甚者 The character 之 is one of the most common characters in Chinese literature and needs frequent explanation. In this chapter, it is first placed after 鬱, which is not depression in the emotional sense, but points to a deficient and stagnant condition. 甚者, which turns *extreme* into a noun is best thought of as *extreme cases*. The character 之 has the function of linking two nouns and in this case, it is linking 鬱 with 甚者. The meaning of this phrase is d*epression's extreme cases* or *those with extreme depression*.

The character 之 in 治之奈何, and its appearance through the rest of this chapter's text, is the pronoun usage of *it*. The characters 治之 mean *treat it*, with the *it* being the entire phrase 鬱之甚者, or *extreme cases of depression*. The entire question means *Extreme cases of depression, how are they treated?* or *How are extreme cases of depression treated?*

4. 奈何 is used throughout the 難經 and 內經. The emphasis of these characters is slightly different from the phrase 何也 in that 奈何 is asking about how to solve a problem or a dilemma. These two phrases are similar in that they are asking for more information about the characters that precede it, but the expected answer for each is slightly different.

5. The series of five phrases that begin with 木鬱達之 are quite simple in their grammar and represent a much more direct way of presenting information. This sentence means *depressed wood-outthrust it* or put more simply, *outthrust depressed wood*. There is a tendency to read this sentence in a much more polite manner: *if wood is depressed, then outthrust it*. This would read 木鬱則達之 in classical Chinese. While this is not a huge error, the feeling of the Chinese is much more direct and the character 則 is not used in a command or instruction.

Examples:

a. 身寒發之。

shēn hàn fā zhī.

Effuse cold bodies.

Use the releasing method to treat cold bodies.

b. 氣鬱調之。

qì yù tiáo zhī.

Regulate depressed qi.

c. 鬱之甚者泄之。

yù zhī shèn zhě xiè zhī.

Drain those with extreme depression.

6. 然 has been covered in previous chapters when a new speaker is about to answer a question. In this chapter, the core meaning of *it's like this* is still present; however, in this chapter it is pointing to a past statement instead of a coming statement. Qi Bo is saying that after one of the previous five treatment methods are complete *like this*, then the next step can occur. There is no change in speaker here. Qi Bo simply gives the next step of his instructions—to regulate the qi after one of the five previous methods has been used.

Translation

The Yellow Emperor asked Qi Bo: How are those with extreme depression treated? Qi Bo said: Outthrust depressed wood. Effuse depressed fire. Strip depressed earth by force. Disperse depressed metal. Fracture (break) depressed water. When this is done, regulate their qi.

This character is known in Chinese medicine for its relationship to the five phases of 火 (fire), 土 (earth), 金 (metal), 水 (water), and 木 (wood). On the left is the radical 彳, which represents a step or a movement. On the right is 亍, the opposite of 彳, and represents a stopping action. Within one character, we have two parts with opposite meanings of step and stop, or movement and rest. The use of the word *phase* suits this character well and explains why the use of *element* is not accurate in translation. 行 is also used as both a verb and noun to represent walking.

Chapter Eleven

中風之病愚意謂邪之所湊
其氣必虛外感者入而有之
東垣治中風專治本而不治
風可謂至當不易之論學者
必須以陰虛陽虛為主

1. 中風之病，愚意謂邪之所湊。其氣必虛。外感者入而有之。
   zhòng fēng zhī bìng, yú yì wèi xié zhī suǒ còu. qí qì bì xū. wài gǎn zhě rù ér yǒu zhī.

2. 東垣治中風專治本而不治風。可謂至當不易之論。學者必須以陰虛陽虛爲主。
   dōngyuán zhì zhòng fēng fū zhì běn ér bù zhì fēng. kě wèi zhì dàng bùyì zhī lùn. xuézhě bì xū yǐ yīnxū yángxū wéi zhǔ.

Vocabulary

1.	中風	zhòng fēng	to be struck by wind to have a stroke
2.	風	fēng	wind
3.	愚	yú	I, me stupid
4.	意	yì	opinion
5.	邪	xié	evil
6.	湊	còu	to gather, to accumulate
7.	必	bì	certainly, surely, invariably
8.	外感	wài gǎn	external influence
9.	入	rù	to enter
10.	東垣	Dōng-yuán	short for 李 (lǐ) 東垣, a famous 13th century physician

11.	尃	fū	to state
12.	本	běn	root, origin
13.	不	bù	not; a negative particle
14.	可謂	kě wèi	one can say; it may be called
15.	可	kě	can, able to, possible to
16.	至當	zhì dàng	most suitable, most appropriate
17.	不易	bù yì	unchanging
	易	yì	to change, to exchange easy, simple
18.	論	lùn	theory, discussion, discourse to discuss (a specific topic)
19.	學	xué	to study, to learn
20.	必須	bì xū	must, have to
21.	爲主	wéi zhǔ	to consider primary

Notes

1. 愚意謂 The root meaning of 愚 is *stupid*. The meaning here, however, is *I* or *me*. Throughout Chinese literature, this is a humble way for the author to refer to himself, especially before making statements that are strong or opinionated. 意 (yì) was covered in Chapter Seven where it represented one of the five 神 (shén). The root meaning of this character is *thinking*, but it can also be used to mean *opinion*. The combinations of 愚意 implies *in my humble opinion*. The author needs to give action to his opinion and therefore uses 謂, meaning *to say*.

2. 邪之所湊 The character 所 changes the verb that follows it into an object. Remember that one of the functions of 之 is to connect two nouns. Whenever the characters 之所 appear together, the verb that follows will inevitably need a place to carry out its action. Although this can often be thought of as *the place where*, this will not always work in translation. In the sentence 邪之所湊, the character 邪 is a noun meaning *evil* and 湊 is a verb meaning *to accumulate*.

Examples:

a. 氣之所會

qì zhī suǒ huì

the place where qi gathers / the gathering place of qi

b. 腎者骨之所生也。

shèn zhě gǔ zhī suǒ shēng yě.

The kidney is the place where bones are generated.

c. 肝者血之所藏也。

gān zhě xuè zhī suǒ cáng yě.

The liver is the place where blood is stored.

3. 人 and 入 look very similar, which may cause confusion when looking at classical texts. These characters are a mirror image of each other. 人 (rén) means *human* and is a picotgraph of the human trunk and two legs. 入 (rù) is a pictograph of roots going into the ground and means *to enter*. The small line at the top of 入 typically occurs only in computer fonts. Compare the two characters as they appear in the first page of this chapter for a more accurate representation of how they will look in classical writing.

4. 不 is a negative particle meaning *not* and is followed by a verb or an adjective. If the character following 不 seems to be a noun, then the author is using it as a verb or an adjective. Oftentimes, if an adjective follows 不, then it can be thought of as the prefix *un-*. If a verb follows 不, the sentence will not end in 也.

Examples:

a. 不治其病則死。
bù zhì qí bìng zé sǐ.
If his disease is not treated, then death (will occur).

b. 岐伯不問其故。
qíbó bù wèn qí gù.
Qi Bo didn't ask (for) his reason.

c. 愚者不知腎有一。
yúzhě bù zhī shèn yǒu yī.
Stupid people don't know the kidney has only one (entity).

5. 可 is followed by a verb to express the ability to carry out the action of that verb. 謂 means *to say* or *to call*, and when 可 is placed in front of it means *can say*. In classical Chinese, the subject of a sentence may be unwritten and as a result, the

reader must figure out the subject based on context. In this sentence, the unnamed subject could be anyone. Readers may mistakenly think 東垣 is the subject, but this would mean *Dong-yuan can say this is a completely suitable and unchanging theory*. The phrase 可謂 rarely has a subject and implies *one can say* or *I (the author) would say*.

Examples:

a. 其病可治也。
   qí bìng kě zhì yě.
   Her disease can be treated.

b. 可謂是不知也。
   kě wèi shì bù zhī yě.
   One can say that this is ignorance.

c. 鬱之甚者，不可發之。
   yù zhī shèn zhě, bù kě fā zhī.
   Extreme cases of depression cannot be effused.

6. Four character phrases, known as 成語 (chéng yǔ), are common in later classical Chinese writing and come from stories, proverbs, or history. Because of this, many of them cannot be easily understood by looking at the characters individually. The example in this chapter, however, follows the meaning of the characters exactly. 至 means *to arrive* and 當 means *suitable* in this context. When 不 is added to 易 it becomes *unchanging*. Unlike most 成語, the characters 至當 and 不易 have their own meanings and were combined to create this four character phrase.

7. 以...爲主 As mentioned before, the character 以 can be used in a variety of ways. In this pattern, 以 precedes a noun, but the English meaning *by means of* or *with* no longer works well. 爲主 means *give first place to* or *give first priority to.* The noun or noun phrase between 以 and 爲主 is what is considered to be the priority. In the sentence 學者必須**以陰虛陽虛爲主**, the two items considered priority are 陰虛 and 陽虛. Examples:

a. 愚以鬱者爲主。

yú yǐ yù zhě wéi zhǔ.

I consider those with depression to be top priority.

b. 學者必須以內經爲主。

xuézhě bì xū yǐ nèi jīng wéi zhǔ.

Students must consider the *Inner Cannon* most important

c. 醫皆以生命爲主。

yī jiē yǐ shēng mìng wéi zhǔ.

Physicians all consider life most important.

Translation

In my humble opinion, the disease being stuck by wind is (due to) the gathering of evil. Their (those struck) qi is invariably deficient. External influences enter and then there is this. (Li) Dong-yuan, (in) treating being struck by wind, stated 'treat the root but not wind.' It can be said that this is a completely suitable and unchanging theory. Students must consider yin deficiency and yang deficiency as top priority.

The outer part of this character presents as a modified version of 凡, which resembles a three-sided container and movement. On the inside, a modified 虫 represents small living matter. Interestingly, the character used most often for insects is 蟲, which includes three of the above characters. The concept of wind is expressed not as something dead, but a moving force that contains within it all kinds of small, living matter. This matter, represented by 虫, if moved from place to place has the potential of affecting the human body. In classical texts, the disease called 中風 was a serious condition. Later manuals that list prescriptions for specific diseases were arranged by diseases and 中風 is almost always the first condition listed. This is not the condition now called a "wind invasion," which resembles the common cold. This disease looks more like sudden paralysis or coma and in modern terms would include a stroke.

Unit Three

Chapter Twelve

從來火字內經有壯火少火
之名後人則曰天火人火君
火相火龍火雷火種種不一
而朱丹溪復以虛實二字括
之可謂善言火矣

從來火字，內經有壯火，少火之名。後人則曰: 天火，人火，君火，相火，龍火，雷火。種種不一，而朱丹溪復以虛實二字揞之。可謂善言火矣。

cóng lái huǒ zì, nèi jīng yǒu zhuànghuǒ, shǎohuǒ zhī míng. hòu rén zé yuē: tiānhuǒ, rénhuǒ, jūnhuǒ, xiànghuǒ, lónghuǒ, léihuǒ. zhǒng zhǒng bù yī. ér Zhū Dān-xī fù yǐ xū shí èr zì shě zhī. kě wèi shàn yǎn huǒ yǐ.

Vocabulary

1.	從來	cóng lái	from earlier up until (a time) previously, formerly
2.	字	zì	Chinese character
3.	內經	nèi jīng	*Inner Classic*, short for the *Yellow Emperor's Inner Classic*
4.	壯	zhuàng	vigorous, strong
5.	後人	hòu rén	later generations
	後	hòu	back, behind after, later
6.	則	zé	particle that sets up a contrast
7.	君	jūn	ruler, sovereign, gentleman
8.	相	xiàng	minister
9.	龍	lóng	dragon, imperial

10. 雷	léi	thunder, disaster
11. 種種	zhǒng zhǒng	each one, every type
種	zhǒng	type, kind, species
12. 不一	bù yī	are different; literally *not one*
13. 朱丹溪	Zhū Dān-xī	a Song Dynasty physician who lived from 1281-1358
14. 復	fù	again; over and over to turn over, to answer
15. 捨	shě	reject, give up, abandon
16. 善	shàn	good; an expert at
17. 矣	yǐ	an end particle for completion, change, or emphasis

Notes

1. Many of the grammar patterns found in Unit Three will be repeated more than once throughout the unit. Study each chapter's grammar well before moving onto the next chapter.

2. 則 acts similarly to the character 者 in this chapter, as it marks the previous character(s). However, 則 marks the beginning of a contrast or comparison. 後人 literally means *after people* and translates as *later generations*. The function of 則 in this chapter is to let readers know that later generations are about to be compared to what is written in the 内經.

The purpose is to mark a coming contrast between the subject marked by 則 and the previously mentioned subject(s).
Examples:

a. 内經曰命門者目*也。難經則曰命門者友腎何也？
nèi jīng yuē mìng mén zhě mù yě. nán jīng zé yuē mìng mén zhě yòu shèn hé yě?
The *Inner Classic* says, "The life gate is the eyes." How is it that the *Classic of Difficulties* says, "The life gate is the right kidney"?
*目 (mù) eye, the eyes

b. 東垣專治本而不治風。愚則謂治本然後治風。
Dōng-yuán fū zhì běn ér bù zhì fēng. yú zé wèi zhìběn ránhòu zhì fēng.
Dong-yuan stated 'treat the root and not wind.' I say treat the root and then treat wind.

3. 種 can be repeated and written as 種種 to change the meaning significantly. Alone, the character 種 means *type* or *kind*. When written twice, however, it becomes *every kind*. Not all nouns can be used in this way, but 種種 and 人人 (everyone), which appears in the next chapter, are both commonly used in this way.

4. In this selection, 不 is followed by 一, which most commonly represents the number one. The meaning of 一 can be extended from the number *one* to an adjective meaning *oneness* or *the same*, but is rarely used in this way without inserting 不 before it. Together, 不一 means *not the same* or *different*. The character 不 can negate adjectives, but 非 cannot, so the sentence 種種非一也 would mean *each type is not (the number) one*.

5. 而朱丹溪復以虛實二字捨之 is another complicated sentence, which makes more sense broken down as follows:

而	ér	and then
朱丹溪	Zhū Dān-xī	Zhu Dan-xi (name)
復	fù	again
以	yǐ	with, by means of
虛實	xū shí	deficiency and excess
二字	èr zì	(these) two characters
捨之	shě zhī	to abandon them (previous ways of naming fire)

The character 復 has many possible translations, all of which fit fairly well in this passage: *again* expresses that fire is again being discussed; *to answer* refers to the response of this physician; *to turn over* shows that there is yet another way to talk about fire which differs from the way it was talked about in the 內經 and by 後人.

The character 以 follows the pattern outlined in Chapter Five, Note 8, where a noun or a group of nouns precedes it. The use of the characters 二字 puts emphasis on the two characters,虛 and 實, which are used to replace all previously mentioned ways of speaking about fire. Even though this is not a necessary addition to construct a grammatically correct sentence, the author uses it to highlight the importance of these two characters replacing all others.

The character 捨 means *to abandon* or *to give up*. 之 is added after this to create the phrase *to abandon them* or *to give them up*. The character 之 means *them* here and is referring back to all of the previous ways fire was discussed. In other words, Zhu Dan-xi talked about 虛火 and 實火, but abandoned discussions of all the other types of fire mentioned in this passage.

6. 善 means *good* and can be used as an adjective describing nouns or an adverb describing verbs. Usually when describing a verb, the author is pointing out that the subject is *good at* the verb (see Example b). Additionally, 善 can be a noun meaning *goodness*. Most adjectives can also be used as adverbs in classical Chinese, but because 善 can be a noun, adjective, or adverb, it must be interpreted carefully when it appears.

Examples:

a. 君知病人之善。
jūn zhī bìng rén zhī shàn.
The gentleman knows the goodness of sick people.

b. 岐伯善治病也。
Qí Bó shàn zhì bìng yě.
Qi Bo is good at treating illness.

c. 上醫治本而不治邪。
shàng yī zhì běn ér bù zhì xié.
Good physicians treat the root but not evil.

7. 矣 English, as a tense based language, changes its verbs to clarify whether something happened in the past, is happening in the present, or will happen in the future. Classical Chinese is an aspect based language and does not change the tense of its verbs; therefore, characters such as 矣 need to be used to help this become clearer to the reader. 矣 most commonly indicates either the completion of an action or a change in state. In this case, the author is likely using this character for both purposes. First, he believes that there

is finally a good way to talk about fire, which there was not before. This indicates a change in the way fire can be talked about. He could also be pointing out that there is a good way to talk about fire and the need to further discuss it has come to an end. Even though linguists separate 矣 into its many functions to help learners understand how it is used, knowing that it shows completion or change is sufficient.

Translation

Originally, the *Inner Classic* had the names vigorous fire and minor fire (within the text). In contrast, later generations spoke of Celestial Fire, Human Fire, Ruler Fire, Ministerial Fire, Dragon Fire, and Thunder Fire. Each type is not the same, and then Zhu Dan-xi used vacuity and repletion (fire) to give these up. One can say (this is a) good way to speak about fire.

This character is common in a variety of classical Chinese texts and outside of medicine refers to the king or to a nobleman who has widespread respect. This is also the character Confucius used to refer to the ideal man. When used in this way, it is often translated into *gentleman*. Within medicine, it most often refers to the heart, the organ that is said to be the ruler of the organs. This character contains 尹, which means *to rule*, and 口, which means mouth; therefore, its meaning is to rule by giving orders.

Chapter Thirteen

乃人人宗其說而於治火卒無定見何也予因易數字以解之夫實火者六淫之邪飲食之傷自外而入勢猶賊也

乃人人宗其說，而於治火卒無定見何也？予因易數字以解之。夫實火者六淫之邪，飲食之傷，自外而入，勢猶賊也。

nǎi rén rén zōng qí shuō, ér yú zhì huǒ cù wú dìng jiàn hé yě? yú yīn yì shù zì yǐ jiě zhī. fú shíhuǒ zhě liù yín zhī xié, yǐn shí zhī shāng, zì wài ér rù, shíyóu zéi yě.

Vocabulary

1.	乃	nǎi	then, thereupon
2.	人人	rén rén	everyone
3.	宗	zōng	to model; to take as a model
4.	說	shuō	words, theory to persuade
5.	卒	cù	suddenly, quickly
6.	無定見	wú ding jiàn	unsure how to proceed, irresolute, without perspective
	定見	ding jiàn	set view, definite opinion
7.	予	yú	I, me to give (rare)
8.	因	yīn	cause, reason, because rely upon, therefore, thereupon
9.	解	jiě	to explain
10.	夫	fú	now, that; now that, now then

11. 六淫	liù yín	six excesses
12. 飲食	yǐn shí	diet, literally *drink and food*
13. 自	zì	from, self, naturally
14. 外	wài	outside, outer
15. 勢猶	shì yóu	resembles, seems like
勢	shì	power, strength, influence certainly
猶	yóu	seems like, similar to; still, even
16. 賊	zéi	thief, robber, enemy

Notes

1. 乃 is another character which often means *then*. At times, this character can also mean *thereupon*, *and*, *but*, or *so*, among other possibilities. Similar to the character 而, the translation of 乃 depends on its context. This character differs from 而 in that its purpose is to either show emotion or to introduce new information—or both. The sentence beginning with 乃 has been translated as if all of these meaning were the intention, which follows the overall feeling of this section. *Then* is the first word of the translation and the word *just* is added for the emotion the author was trying to convey.

2. 其說 The character 其 is a possessive pronoun, indicating that the following character must be a noun. The character 說 can be used as either a noun or a verb. Luckily, the

appearance of 其 before 說 makes it easy to see that 說 is being used as a noun meaning *words*.

3. 於 In this chapter, we have a new use for the character 於, which was already discussed in Chapter Ten, Note 2. When placed before a verb, as it is in the phrase 於治火, the meaning is *at treating fire* or *in treating fire*. The examples below are just some of the ways 於 is commonly used.

Examples:

a. 君善於治火也。
jūn shàn yú zhì huǒ yě.
The ruler is an expert at treating fire.

b. 帝於朱丹溪解之。
dì yú Zhū Dān-xī jiě zhī.
The emperor explained it to Zhu Dan-xi.

The character 於 is also used to mean *than* when making comparisons. When using 於 in this way, the character before it must be an adjective.

c. 有病者少於無病者。
yǒu bìng zhě shǎo yú wú bìng zhě.
There are less people with disease than there are without.

d. 無病者多於有病者。
wú bìng zhě duō yú yǒu bìng zhě.
There are more people without disease than with disease.

4. Determining which phrase 何也 is specifically asking about in this text may be difficult. In previous chapters, the question marker 何也 requested more information from another person. In this chapter, the question is rhetorical and shows a bit of shock. The author is expressing his dissatisfaction by asking 'How could people read the words of 朱丹溪 and not

know how to proceed?' The author then states he will use a *simple* explanation to make this clearer. Other grammar particles show more of shock than this one, yet here the author is clearly annoyed that anything must be explained further and therefore asks 何也— *how could it be?*

5. 夫 placed at the beginning of a sentence is best thought of as *now then*. Imagine a college professor who has just given a series of statements and to introduce something that further explains those statements, he begins a sentence with *now then*. The feeling of the character 夫 is similar to this.

6. 六淫 are often referred to as the *six pathogenic influences*, but the original Chinese meaning is closer to the *six excesses*.

a. 熱 (rè) heat
b. 寒 (hán) cold
c. 乾 (gān) dry
d. 濕 (shī) damp
e. 風 (fēng) wind
f. 暑 (shǔ) summer-heat

7. 者. . .也 While this pattern has been covered several times, in this instance the number of characters and clauses between these two characters are numerous. The characters between 者 and 也 are meant to define the subject, which in this case is 實火, or *excess fire*. When reading such long sentences in classical Chinese, it is best to break down the series of phrases that occur. The author clarifies 實火 as:

1. 六淫之邪 — the evil of the six excesses
2. 飲食之傷 — injury by (poor diet)
3. 自外而入 — enters from the outside
4. 勢猶賊 — resembles a robber

也 is used to bring this all together. This sentence could be translated into English in a number of ways and is an example of how focusing on the Chinese grammar is more effective than trying to understand classical Chinese through English translation.

8. 自 is often used in Chinese medical texts as a full verb. In this chapter and the next, this character means *from*, but is classified as a verb. The sentence 自外而入 can be translated as *comes from the outside then enters* or *enters from the outside*. It is difficult to express the verbal aspect of this character in English.

9. 勢猶 is used when the author is about to make an analogy. In later medical texts, the use of analogy is employed regularly as a teaching tool. The use of this phrase is absent in the 内經 and 難經. The characters 猶, *resembles*, and 勢, *power* or *influence*, combine to create the phrase *strong resemblance*. This phrase is key to understanding the following chapters. The author wants to use an analogy for excess fire resembling a robber, and later deficient fire resembling a child.

Translation

Then everyone just took his words as a model, but in treating fire, they were suddenly uncertain how to proceed. How could this be? I will therefore rely upon a few simple words so as to explain this. Now then, excess fire is the evil of the six pathogenic influences (and) dietary injury. It enters from the outside and resembles a robber.

This character was originally a pictograph character resembling a lizard, showing its head 日 and legs 勿. This may explain its more ancient meaning of *change*, which appears in the classic *The Book of Changes*, or 易經 (yì jīng). This character also commonly means *easy*, the opposite of the character 難 (nán), which appears in the medical classic *The Classic of Difficulties*, or 難經.

Chapter Fourteen

賊可驅而不可留賊至則驅之如消散清涼攻伐等藥皆可按法取用虛火者七情色慾勞役耗神自內而發勢猶子也

賊可驅而不可留。賊至則驅之。如消散清涼攻伐等藥皆可按法取用。虛火者七情，色慾，勞役，耗神，自內而發，勢猶子也。

zéi kě qū ér bù kě liú. zéi zhì zé qū zhī. rú xiāo sàn qīng liáng gōng fá děng yào jiē kě àn fă qŭ yòng. xūhuŏ zhě qī qíng, sè yù, láo yì, hào shén, zì nèi ér fā, shìyóu zĭ yě.

Vocabulary

1.	驅	qū	to expel, to drive away
2.	留	liú	to remain, to leave (in place)
3.	如	rú	to be like, such as, if
4.	消	xiāo	to disperse
5.	散	sàn săn	to dissipate, to scatter powdered medicine
6.	清	qīng	to clear; clear
7.	涼	liáng	to cool; cool
8.	攻	gōng	to attack
9.	伐	fá	to cut down, to quell
10.	藥	yào	medicine
11.	按法	àn fă	according to (proper) methods

	按	àn	according to
	法	fǎ	method
12.	取用	qǔ yòng	select and use
	取	qǔ	to select, to adopt
	用	yòng	to use, to apply
13.	七情	qī qíng	seven emotions
	情	qíng	emotion(s), affection, love
14.	色慾	sè yù	sexual lust
	色	sè	color, expression
	慾	yù	desire, lust, passion, greed
15.	勞役	láo yì	hard labor, overwork
	役	yì	labor, service
16.	耗	hào	consume, waste
17.	子	zǐ	child, seed

Notes

1. 可 verb 而不可 verb This grammar pattern is used to give instructions and is therefore quite common in medical texts. The character 可 must be followed by a verb and in this case expresses that this action can be taken. The verb following 不可 is an action that cannot be taken. In the sentence 賊可驅而不可留, the character 驅 means *to expel* and 留 means *to leave* or to leave something where it was found. This sentence translates as *a robber can be expelled but cannot be left (to steal).*

Examples:

a. 實火可泄而不可調。
   shíhuǒ kě xiè ér bù kě tiáo.
   Excess fire can be drained but cannot be regulated.

b. 肝鬱可達而不可發。
   gān yù kě dá ér bù kě fā.
   Liver depression (stagnation) can be thrust out but cannot be effused (released).

c. 諸陰可治而不可發。
   zhū yīn kě zhì ér bù kě fā.
   The yin (vessels) can be treated but they cannot be released.

2. 如 means *like* or *such as* and comes before examples. In this passage, and the passage in Chapter Fifteen, 如 is followed by examples of herbs that fit the strategy which resembles chasing away a robber. Used at the beginning of a sentence and in combination with 則, the character 如 means *if* (see Chapter Fifteen, Note 3).

3. 等藥 The character 等 (děng) means *class* or *group*; therefore, 等藥 would refer to the group of herbs that belong to the categories just discussed, which are 消散清涼攻伐 (xiāo sàn qīng liáng gōng fá). The character 等 is used in a similar way to the character 諸 (zhū) in that each is used as an adjective to describe the noun that follows it. In most classical texts, meridians were not arranged according to their relationships with the 藏府, but with their correspondences to 陰陽 (for example, 手少陰). Similarly, herbs were not categorized by their affect on 藏府 patterns as they are in many modern texts, but with groups or categories that performed a specific function. 等藥 refers to the categories of herbs which can be used to treat 實火 (shí huǒ). The text of Chapter Fifteen will list the categories of herbs that can be used to treat 虛火 (xū huǒ).

4. 按法 In the sentence 皆可按法取用, the character 皆 (jiē) means *all* and points to the methods just discussed. The character 可 (kě) makes an important distinction—all of these herbs *may* be chosen but they are **not** all meant to be chosen at once. The character 按 means *according to* and 法 is a *method* or *technique*. After deciding excess fire has afflicted a person, this author's method is to choose one of the proper methods from the following list. After this, he would choose herbs from the category he has decided to use, which must also fit the pattern.

Translation

A robber can be expelled but cannot be left in place. If a robber arrives, then expel him. Medicines from categories such as dispersing, dissipating, clearing, cooling, attacking, and quelling can all be used according to the (proper) method. Deficient fire is (due to) the seven emotions, sexual lust, hard labor, and consumption of the spirit. It emanates from the inside and strongly resembles a child.

The medicinal products that can be ingested are represented by this character, while the character 醫 (yī) represents medicine as a concept. This character uses the grass radical just as the character 藏 does. The character under this radical is 樂, which means *happiness*. The overall meaning of this character is plants that make people happy, or *medicine*. Used alone, this character refers to individual plants. For prescriptions, or combinations of medicinal plants, the characters 藥方 (yào fāng) are used.

Chapter Fifteen

子可養而不可害子逆則安之如補氣滋水理脾等藥皆可按法施用夫子者奉身之本也若以驅賊者驅其子則無以爲養神生命之本矣人固不可認賊作子更不可認子作賊

子可養而不可害。子逆則安之。如補氣，滋水，理脾等藥。皆可按法施用。夫子者奉身之本也。若以驅賊者驅其子，則無以爲養神生命之本矣。人固不可認賊作子，更不可認子作賊。

zǐ kě yǎng ér bù kě hài. zǐ nì zé ān zhī. rú bǔ qì, zī shuǐ, lǐ pí děng yào jiē kě àn fǎ shī yòng. fú zǐ zhě fèng shēn zhī běn yě. ruò yǐ qū zéi zhě qū qí zǐ, zé wú yǐ wéi yǎng shén shēng mìng zhī běn yǐ. rén gù bù kě rèn zéi zuò zǐ, gèng bù kě rèn zǐ zuò zéi.

Vocabulary

1.	養	yǎng	to nourish, support, to raise
2.	害	hài	to harm
3.	逆	nì	to disobey, contrarian (to rules)
	順	shùn	to obey, to follow
4.	安	ān	to pacify, to quiet peace
5.	補	bǔ	to supplement, to benefit
6.	滋	zī	to add, to increase, to enrich
7.	理	lǐ	to regulate, to rectify
8.	施用	shī yòng	to use, to employ
9.	奉	fèng	esteemed, to respectfully receive

10. 若	ruò	if, to be like, such as interchangeable with 如
11. 無以爲	wú yǐ wéi	no way to, no means to
12. 生命	shēng mìng	life
13. 固	gù	certainly, definitely
14. 認	rèn	to recognize, to identify
15. 作	zuò	to regard as, to take for
16. 更	gèng	even more, moreover

Notes

1. This and the previous chapter depict two different ways of writing *use*. Numerous possible characters exist that can come before 用 to express *using*. This author chooses 取用 and 施用 at the end of two very similar sentence patterns. The character 取 (qǔ) means *to select*, while the character 施 (shī) means *to employ*. The phrases 取用 and 施用 were likely selected simply so that the author was not being overly repetitive in his writing.

2. 奉身 uses 奉, which means to *receive or give something with great respect*. In former times, and in some places up to today, the physical body was seen as something bestowed upon a person from their ancestors and was therefore to be respected. Typically this way of looking at the body is considered a Confucian view, but was so predominant in the

early history of China that there is difficulty saying that it belonged to only one school of thought. When writing about and making statements about the body, this and other similar characters can be found.

3. 若...則 In this text, the character 若 means *if.* The character 則 also creates an *if* in the clause preceding it, making the use of 若 seem repetitive. The character 若 is often added to sentences which contain long phrases before and after 則. The characters between 若 and 則 are the cause, which must occur before the result described after 則. The *if* clause of this sentence reads 若以驅賊者驅其子:

若	if
以	with (when a noun follows)
驅賊者	substances that chase away robbers
驅其子	chase away their child

Look at the characters 驅賊者 together. 者 turns 驅賊 into a noun which means *substances that chase away robbers.* Remember that 驅賊 is being used in an analogy and the overall subject of this passage is the use of medicinal substances. 驅賊者 is referring back to the herbs in the categories of 消散清涼攻伐.

The verb phrase 驅其子 means *to chase away their child.* 其 is referring to an unnamed patient being given those herbs. This part of the sentence means *If one chases out the child with items that chase out robbers...*

4. 則...矣 This pattern expresses a change that comes about because the conditions before 則 are met to produce the result described after it. One of the functions of the end particle 矣 (yǐ) is to mark a change in state. Although the first clause, explained above, is a necessary part of this grammar pattern, it will not always start with the character 若. For example, the sentences 若從陰陽則生 and 從陰陽則生 are the same.

The second part of this sentence reads 則無以爲養神生命之本矣:

則	if...then
無以爲	there is no way to
養神	support the spirit
(養) 生命之本	support the root of life
矣	end particle (change in state)

Although 無以爲 can be broken down further to understand its grammar components, it may simply be thought of as a phrase meaning *there is no way to*. The verb 養 is modifying to two different nouns, namely 神 and 生命之本. Verbs can often be found modifying more than one noun in this way. The character 矣 is added at the end to mark a change in state. This part of the sentence means *then there is no way to support the spirit or the roots of life.*

Another way to write the sentence 若以驅賊者驅其子, 則無以爲養神生命之本矣 without the use of analogy would be: 若以消散清涼攻伐等薬治虛火, 則無以爲養神生命之本矣. The use of analogy in this case is a way to explain concepts that are difficult to understand directly.

5. Several characters are used as adverbs meaning *must* or expressing an imperative, including 固 in this chapter and 必 (bì) and 必須 (bì xū) from Chapter Eleven. The characters 必 and 固 have the same basic meaning of *must* or *have to* when followed by verbs. Both characters can be preceded by the negative 不 (bù) when an author wants to express the negative aspect of this (need not). 必須 can be followed by a verb, but it is never preceded by 不. It can also act as a verb by itself and there is no way to give an equivalent English meaning for this, as the context is the only sure way to know what the author is expressing.

6. 認...作 The character 認 means *to recognize* and 作 has many possible uses, but within this pattern is best thought of as *to regard as*. In the selection above, this pattern appears twice, with the first instance reading 認賊作子, which means *to recognize a robber as a child.*

Examples:

a. 認攻之藥作補氣之藥
rèn gōng zhī yào zuò bǔqì zhī yào
to identify attacking medicine as qi-supporting medicine

b. 學者不可認表作裏。
xuézhě bù kě rèn biǎo zuò lǐ.
Students cannot regard the exterior as the interior.

c. 若認虛作實，則無以爲治其病矣。
ruò rèn xū zuò shí, zé wúyǐwéi zhì qí bìng yǐ.
If deficiency is recognized as excess, then it will be impossible to treat her disease.

The final sentence, 人固不可認賊作子更不可認子作賊, is used as an analogy and could also be written: 人固不可認實火作虛火, 更不可認虛火作實火.

Translation

A child can be raised but cannot be harmed. If a child's behavior is contrary (to the usual behavior) then pacify him. Medicines from categories such as building qi, enriching water, and rectifying the spleen can all be used according to the (proper) method. Now then, children are the roots of our esteemed bodies. If (one) expels the child with those items which expel robbers, then there will be no way to support the spirit or the roots of life. People can certainly not identify a robber as a child, and even more so, cannot recognize a child as a robber.

The origins of this character potentially mean *sheep food.* The upper part of this character is 羊 (yáng), which means *sheep.* The lower part is 食 (shí), which was covered earlier and means *food* or *to eat.* This character represents *caring for livestock.* Sheep and other grazing animals were an important part of early Chinese culture. Sheep, in particular, would have provided not just meat, but also their wool. This character has come to mean *to raise,* as in raising children or animals. 養 has many uses in both medicine and religion. The characters 養神 (yǎng shén), for example, can have meanings ranging from *resting to refresh one's spirits* to a variety of Daoist spiritual practices that *revive the spirit.* There are a group of practices collectively referred to as 養生 (yǎng shēng) which mix religious, dietary and medical practices to extend and improve one's life.

Appendices

Appendix I

Texts in Simplified Characters

Chapter One

医小道也.
医之治病也.
从阴阳则生.

Chapter Two

三焦者水鼓之道路也.
身有表里上下之别焉.

Chapter Three

有命门然后生心. 心主血. 有心然后生肺. 肺主皮毛. 有肺然后生肾. 肾主骨髓. 有肾则与命门合二数.

Chapter Four

有陽火, 有陰火. 有水中之火, 有土中之火. 有金中之火, 有木中之火. 陽火者天上之日月之火. 陰火者虛火. 此對待之火也.

Chapter Five

脏各有一耳. 肾独有两者何也? 然. 肾两者非皆肾也. 其左者为肾, 右者为命门. 故男子以藏精, 女子以系胞. 故知肾有一也.

Chapter Six

难经二十五曰: 有十二经, 五脏, 六府, 十一耳. 其一经者何等经也? 然. 一经者手少阴与心主别脉也. 心主与三焦为表里. 具有名而无形. 故言经有十二也.

Chapter Seven

五脏所藏: 心藏神, 肺藏魄, 肝藏魂, 脾藏意, 肾藏志. 是谓五脏所藏. 五脏所主: 心主脉, 肺主皮, 肝主筋, 脾主肉, 肾主骨. 是谓五主. 五劳所伤: 久视伤血, 久卧伤气, 久坐伤肉, 久立伤骨, 久行伤筋. 是谓五劳所伤. 五脉应象: 肝脉弦, 心脉钩, 脾脉代, 肺脉毛, 肾脉石. 是谓五藏之脉.

Chapter Eight

人面独能耐寒者何也? 然. 人头者诸阳之会也. 诸阴脉皆至颈胸中而还. 独诸阳脉皆上至头耳. 故令面耐寒也.

Chapter Nine

藏唯有五. 府独有六者何也? 然. 所以府有六者谓三焦也. 有原气之别焉. 主特诸气. 有名而无形. 其经属手少阳. 此外府也. 故言府有六焉.

Chapter Ten

黄帝问于岐伯: 郁之甚者, 治之奈何? 岐伯曰: 木郁达之. 火郁发之. 土郁夺之. 金郁泄之. 水郁折之. 然, 调其气.

Chapter Eleven

中风之病, 愚意谓邪之所凑. 其气必虚. 外感者入而有之. 东垣治中风専治本而不治风. 可谓至当不易之论. 学者必须以阴虚阳虚为主.

Chapter Twelve

从来火字, 内经有壮火, 少火之名. 后人则曰: 天火, 人火, 君火, 相火, 龙火, 雷火. 种种不一，而朱丹溪复以虚实二字舍之. 可谓善言火矣.

Chapter Thirteen

乃人人宗其说, 而于治火卒无定见何也? 予因易数字以解之. 夫实火者六淫之邪, 饮食之伤, 自外而入, 势犹贼也.

Chapter Fourteen

贼可驱而不可留. 贼至则驱之. 如消散, 清凉, 功伐等药皆可按法取用. 虚火者七情, 色欲, 劳役, 耗神, 自内而发, 势犹子也.

Chapter Fifteen

子可养而不可害. 子逆则安之. 如补气, 滋水, 理脾等药皆可按法施用. 夫子者奉身之本也. 若以驱贼者驱其子, 则无以为养神生命之本矣. 人固不可认贼作子, 更不可认子作贼.

Appendix II

Introductory Chapter Notes

Chapter One

The phrase 醫小道也 was first written by the Neo-Confucian philosopher 朱熹 (Zhū Xī), who lived during the Song Dynasty from 1130-1200. He was comparing the study of medicine with greater pursuits (大道), which in his mind included philosophy, government, and ethics. This phrase can be found in many medical manuscripts written after his time, as his teachings dominated Chinese culture for several hundred years after his death.

The phrase 醫之治病 is found in at least three different medical books, including the 黃帝內經. It can also be found in the Wang Chong's 論衡 (lùn héng), which is one of China's earliest works on the philosophy of science, among other topics. This philosopher and his written works were rejected at the time, but Wang was later seen as one of China's great early thinkers.

The phrase 從陰陽則生 first appears in the 內經, but is later to be found in a variety of medical and 養生 texts for centuries.

Chapter Two

The two phrases from this chapter are not as commonly found, but contain grammar and characters essential for studying

classical medical texts. The phrase 三焦者水鼓之道路也 is found in Chapter 31 of the 難經. Later authors had different things to say, including:
三焦者水火之道路也
The triple warmer is the passageway of water and fire.
三焦爲水液運行之道路
The triple warmer is considered the passageway of fluid circulation.
三焦者膀胱之道路也
The triple warmer is the passageway of the urinary bladder.

The phrase 身有表裡上下之別焉 was modified slightly from a passage by 徐靈胎 which originally said 夫人身一也，實有表裡上下之別焉 and has essentially the same meaning. The original line can be directly translated as: *Now, people's bodies are one entity, (they) in fact have distinctions of interior, exterior, upper (and) lower within them.*

Chapter Three

The text from this chapter can be found in a variety of medical texts with a change in just one character, which alters the meaning slightly:
有命門然後生心. 心生血. 有心然後生肺. 肺生皮毛. 有肺然後生腎. 腎生骨髓.

Chapter Four

The original text states: 陰火者燈燭之火. The context of this quote is related to cosmological studies. There was no way to include the entire context of the original text in this book, so 燈燭 was replaced with 虛火. Within medical literature, 陰火 is commonly equated with 虛火.

Appendix III
English Glossary

-A-

abandon	捨	shě
able	能	néng
according to	按	àn
accumulate	湊	còu
after	後	hòu
again	復	fù
all	皆	jiē
alone	獨	dú
alone can	獨能	dú néng
alone has	獨有	dú yǒu
arrive	至	zhì
ascend	上	shàng
ask	問	wèn
attack	攻	gōng

-B-

belong to (category)	屬	shǔ
benefit	補	bǔ
big	大	dà
bind	繫	jì

blood	血	xiě, xuè
body	身	shēn
bone marrow	骨髓	gǔ suǐ
bone(s)	骨	gǔ
both	皆	jiē
break	折	zhé
bright	明	míng

-C-

call	謂	wèi
can say	可謂	kě wèi
cause	因	yīn
ceasing yin	厥陰	jué yīn
center	中	zhōng
certainly	必	bì
certainly	固	gù
change	易	yì
chest	胸	xiōng
child	子	zǐ
Chinese character	字	zì
class	等	děng
class (group)	諸	zhū
classic	經	jīng
clear	清	qīng
cold	寒	hán
color	色	sè
combine	合	hé
considered	爲	wéi
consider primary	爲主	wéi zhǔ

consume	耗	hào
cool	涼	liáng
correspond	應	yīng
count	數	shǔ

-D-

damage	傷	shāng
damp	濕	shī
deal with	對待	duì dài
death	死	sǐ
decree	命	mìng
deficient	虛	xū
definitely	固	gù
depot	藏	zàng
depression	鬱	yù
descend	下	xià
desire	慾	yù
die	死	sǐ
difference	別	bié
different	不一	bù yī
discuss a topic	論	lùn
discussion	論	lùn
disobey	逆	nì
disperse	消	xiāo
distinction	別	bié
dragon	龍	lóng
drain	泄	xiè
drink	飲	yǐn
dry	乾	gān

-E-

each	各	gè
earth	地	dì
earth	土	tǔ
easy	易	yì
eat	食	shí
effuse	發	fā
emotion(s)	情	qíng
endure	耐	nài
enrich	滋	zī
enter	入	rù
essence	精	jīng
esteemed	奉	fèng
even moreso	更	gèng
every type	種種	zhǒng zhǒng
everyone	人人	rén rén
evil	邪	xié
excess	實	shí
expel	驅	qū
explain	解	jiě
exterior	表	biǎo
external influence	外感	wài gǎn
extreme	甚	shèn
eye(s)	目	mù

-F-

face	面	miàn
female	女	nǚ
female	女子	nǚ zi

fire	火	huǒ
flesh	肉	ròu
follow	從	cóng
food	食	shí
foot	足	zú
form	形	xíng
formerly	從來	cóng lái
formless	無形	wú xíng
from	從	cóng
from	自	zì

-G-

gallbladder	膽	dǎn
gate	門	mén
gather	湊	còu
generate	生	shēng
gentleman	君	jūn
give	與	yǔ
good	善	shàn
govern	主	zhǔ
grains	鼓	gǔ
greater	大	dà
group	等	děng

-H-

hair (body hair)	毛	máo
hand	手	shǒu
harm	害	hài
have	有	yǒu

head	頭	tóu
heart	心	xīn
heart master	心主	xīn zhǔ
heat	熱	rè
heaven	天	tiān
hook-like	鉤	gōu
human	人	rén

-I-

I	予	yú
I	愚	yú
illness	病	bìng
image	象	xiàng
inner	內	nèi
Inner Classic	內經	nèi jīng
inspect	視	shì
interior	裏	lǐ
intermittent	代	dài
invariably	必	bì
irresolute	無定見	wú ding jiàn

-K, L-

kidney	腎	shèn
know	知	zhī
labor	役	yì
large intestine	大腸	dà cháng
later	後	hòu
later generations	後人	hòu rén
leave in place	留	liú

left	左	zuǒ
lesser	小	xiǎo
life	生命	shēng mìng
life gate, gate of life	命門	mìng mén
like this	然	rán
live	生	shēng
liver	肝	gān
long (time)	久	jiǔ
look at	視	shì
lower	下	xià
lung	肺	fèi

-M-

make	令	lìng
male	男	nán
males	男子	nán zi
manage	主持	zhǔchí
many	多	duō
marrow	髓	suǐ
medicinals	藥	yào
medicine	醫	yī
meeting place	會	huì
meridian	經	jīng
metal	金	jīn
method	法	fǎ
Ming Dynasty	明	míng
minister	相	xiàng
minor, lesser, few	少	shǎo
minor-yin	少陰	shǎo yīn

model	宗	zōng
moon	月	yuè
more	多	duō
movement	行	xíng
must	必須	bì xū

-N-

neck	頸	jǐng, gěng
not	不	bù
not	非	fēi
not have	無	wú
nourish	養	yǎng
now then	夫	fú
number	數	shù

-O-

obey	順	shùn
only	唯	wéi
only has	唯有	wéi yǒu
only then	然後	rán hòu
opinion	意	yì
opinion (fixed)	定見	ding jiàn
order	命	mìng
origin	本	běn
outer	外	wài
outthrust	達	dá
overwork	勞役	láo yì

-P, Q-

pacify	安	ān
palace	府	fǔ
path	道	dào
pathway	道路	dào lù
peace	安	ān
people	人	rén
persuade	說	shuō
physician	醫	yī
possess	具有	jù yǒu
powder	散	sǎn
Qing Dynasty	清	qīng
quell	伐	fá

-R-

quickly	卒	cù
reason	故	gù
recognize	認	rèn
rectify	理	lǐ
regard as	作	zuò
regulate	理	lǐ
regulate	調	tiáo
release	發	fā
rely upon	因	yīn
replete	實	shí
resembles	勢猶	shì yóu
return	還	huán
right	右	yòu
road	路	lù

rolling pulse	石	shí
root	本	běn
rule	主	zhǔ
ruler	君	jūn

-S-

say	謂	wèi
say	言	yán
say	曰	yuē
scatter	散	sàn
seems like	猶	yóu
select	取	qǔ
set view	定見	ding jiàn
seven emotions	七情	qī qíng
sexual lust	色慾	sè yù
sickness	病	bìng
sit	坐	zuò
six excesses	六淫	liù yín
skin	皮	pí
sky	天	tiān
sky	天上	tiān shàng
sleep	臥	wò
small	小	xiǎo
small intestine	小腸	xiǎo cháng
soil	土	tǔ
soul, animalistic	魄	pò
soul, human	魂	hún
source qi	原氣	yuán qì
spirit	神	shén

spleen	脾	pí
stand	立	lì
state	尃	fū
stomach	胃	wèi
stone-like (pulse)	石	shí
store	藏	cáng
string-like (pulse)	絃	xián
strong	壯	zhuàng
struck by	中	zhòng
study	學	xué
stupid	愚	yú
suddenly	卒	cù
suitable	至當	zhì dàng
summer-heat	暑	shǔ
sun	日	rì
supplement	補	bǔ

-T-

take by force	奪	duó
tendons	筋	jīn
that	彼	bǐ
theory	論	lùn
therefore	故	gù
therefore it is said	故言	gù yán
these	此	cǐ
thief	賊	zéi
thin pulse	毛	máo
this	此	cǐ
this	是	shì

those	彼	bǐ
thought	意	yì
thunder	雷	léi
tie	繫	jì
tool	具	jù
treat	對待	duì dài
treat	治	zhì
triple warmer	三焦	sān jiāo
turn over	復	fù
twenty-five	二十五	èrshíwǔ
two	二	èr
two	兩	liǎng
type	種	zhǒng

-U to Z-

unchanging	不易	bù yì
upper	上	shàng
urinary bladder	膀胱	pang guāng
use	取用	qǔ yòng
use	施用	shī yòng
use	用	yòng
uterus	胞	bāo
vacuous	虛	xū
vessel	脈	mài, mò
walk	行	xíng
waste	耗	hào
water	水	shuǐ
Way, a path	道	dào
what kind of	何等	hé děng

will	志	zhì
wind	風	fēng
wiry pulse	絃	xián
wood	木	mù
words	言	yán
words to persuade	說	shuō
work	勞	láo
yang	陽	yáng
Yellow Emperor	黃帝	huáng dì
yin	陰	yīn
yin motility vessel	陰蹻脈	yīn qiāo mài

Pinyin Index

cáng	藏	to store; Ch. 5; p. 55
chéng yǔ	成語	four character phrase; p. 100
cǐ	此	this, these; Ch. 4; p. 43
cóng	從	from, by means of to follow, to accompany; Ch. 1
cóng lái	從來	from earlier up until (a time) previously, formerly; Ch. 12
còu	湊	to gather, to accumulate; Ch. 11; p. 98
cù	卒	suddenly, quickly; Ch. 13
dá	達	to outthrust; Ch. 10
dà	大	big, greater; Ch. 1
dà cháng	大腸	large intestine; Ch. 6
dài	代	intermittent; Ch. 7
dǎn	膽	gallbladder; Ch. 6
dào	道	the Way, a path; Ch. 1; p. 30
dào lù	道路	pathway; Ch. 2
děng	等	class, ranking, group; Ch. 6; p. 125
dì	地	earth, the ground; Ch. 4
dìng jiàn	定見	set view, definite opinion; Ch. 13
Dōng-yuán	東垣	short for 李東垣, a famous 13th century physician; Ch. 11
dú	獨	alone; Ch. 5; p. 50, 85
dú néng	獨能	alone can; Ch. 8
dú yǒu	獨有	alone has; Ch. 5

gān	乾	dry
gè	各	each, every; Ch. 5
gèng	更	even more, moreover; Ch. 15
gōng	攻	to attack; Ch. 14
gōu	鉤	hook-like; Ch. 7
gǔ	骨	bone(s); Ch. 3
gǔ suǐ	骨髓	bone marrow; Ch. 3
gù	固	certainly, definitely; Ch. 15; p. 132
gù	故	therefore, hence, so reason; Ch. 5; p. 53
gù yán	故言	therefore it is said; Ch. 6
hài	害	to harm; Ch. 15
hán	寒	cold; Ch. 8; p. 78, 81
hán zhě	寒者	the cold, cold things; Ch. 8
hào	耗	consume, waste; Ch. 14
hé	合	combine, mix together; Ch. 3
hé	何	how/what; a question word; Ch. 5; p. 50
hé děng	何等	what kind of, what else; Ch. 6; p. 62
hé yě	何也	How is it that? Why? Ch. 5; p. 51, 62, 116-117
hòu	後	after, behind; Ch. 3
hòu	後	after, later; Ch. 12
hòu rén	後人	later generations; Ch. 12
huán	還	to return (a thing or to a place); Ch. 8

léi	雷	thunder, disaster; Ch. 12
lǐ	裏	interior; Ch. 2
lǐ	理	to regulate, to rectify; Ch. 15
lì	立	to stand; Ch. 7
liáng	涼	to cool; cool; Ch. 14
liǎng	兩	two; Ch. 3; p. 36
lìng	令	to cause, to make, to order also written as 令; Ch. 8; p. 80
liú	留	to remain, to leave (in place); Ch. 14
liù yín	六淫	six excesses; Ch. 13; p. 117
lóng	龍	dragon, imperial; Ch. 12
lù	路	a road; Ch. 2
lùn	論	theory, discussion, discourse to discuss (a specific topic); Ch. 11
mài	脈	vessel, pulse position; Ch. 6
máo	毛	body hair; Ch. 3
máo	毛	thin, hair-like (pulse); Ch. 7
mén	門	gate, door; Ch. 3
miàn	面	face; Ch. 8
míng	明	Ming Dynasty; bright, clear
mìng	命	life, fate, destiny, decree, order to order; Ch. 3; p. 37
mìng mén	命門	life gate, gate of life; Ch. 3
mò	脈	vessel, pulse position; Ch. 6

qì	氣	qi, vapor, function, breath; Ch. 9; p. 88
qīng	清	to clear; clear; Ch. 14 Qing Dynasty
qíng	情	emotion(s), affection, love; Ch. 14
qū	驅	to expel, to drive away; Ch. 14
qǔ	取	to select, to adopt; Ch. 14; p. 129
qǔ yòng	取用	select and use; Ch. 14
rán	然	(to be) like this; Ch. 3, 5; p. 51, 94
rán hòu	然後	only then ; Ch. 3; p. 34-5
rè	熱	heat
rén	人	people, person, human; Ch. 8; p. 99
rén miàn	人面	people's faces; Ch. 8; p. 77
rén rén	人人	everyone; Ch. 13; p. 108
rèn	認	to recognize, to identify; Ch. 15; p. 132
rì	日	day, sun; Ch. 4; p. 61
ròu	肉	flesh, muscles; Ch. 7
rú	如	to be like, such as, if; Ch. 14; p. 124
rù	入	to enter; Ch. 11; p 99
ruò	若	if, to be like, such as interchangeable with 如; Ch. 15; p. 130
sān jiāo	三焦	triple burner, triple warmer; Ch. 2; p. 29
sàn sǎn	散	to dissipate, to scatter powdered medicine; Ch. 14
sè	色	color, expression; Ch. 14

shì wèi	是謂	this is called, this is known as; Ch. 7; p. 71
shì yóu	勢猶	resembles, seems like; Ch. 13; p. 118
shǒu	手	hand; Ch. 6
shǒu jué yīn	手厥陰	the name for the heart master's vessel in modern medical thinking
shǒu shǎo yīn	手少陰	hand minor-yin ; Ch. 6
shǒu xīn zhǔ	手心主	hand heart master, the name for the heart master's vessel in the nán jīng
shǔ	暑	summer-heat
shǔ	屬	to belong to (a category); Ch. 9
shù shǔ	數	number to count, to figure; Ch. 3
shuǐ gǔ	水鼓	water and grains, food and water; Ch. 2
shùn	順	to obey, to follow; Ch. 15
shuō	說	words, theory to persuade; Ch. 13; p. 115-6
sǐ	死	death to die; Ch. 1
sù wèn	素問	*Simple Questions*, one fascicle of the nèi jīng
suǐ	髓	marrow; Ch. 3
suǒ	所	that which is, what is; Ch. 7; p. 70-1, 98, 100
suǒ yǐ	所以	that by which; Ch. 9; p. 86
tiān	天	heaven, the sky; Ch. 4; p. 44
tiān shàng	天上	the sky; Ch. 4

tiáo	調	to regulate; Ch. 10
tóu	頭	head; Ch. 8
tǔ	土	earth, soil; Ch. 4
wài	外	outside, outer; Ch. 9
wài	外	outside, outer; Ch. 13
wài gǎn	外感	external influence; Ch. 11
wài jīng	外經	a lost text of which portions are quoted in other sources; p. 63
wéi	爲	to serve as, is considered; Ch. 5
wéi	唯	only; Ch. 9; p. 85
wéi yǒu	唯有	only have, only has; Ch. 9; p. 85
wéi zhǔ	爲主	to consider primary; Ch. 11; p. 101
wèi	胃	stomach; Ch. 6
wèi	謂	to be called, to say or state; Ch. 7; p. 86, 98
wèn	問	to ask; Ch. 10; p. 91
wèn yú	問於	to ask a question to (person); Ch. 10; p. 91-2
wò	臥	to sleep; Ch. 7
wú	無	does not have, there are no/ none; Ch. 2; p. 65
wú dìng jiàn	無定見	unsure how to proceed, irresolute, without perspective; Ch. 13
wú xíng	無形	formless (lit. without form); Ch. 6
wú yǐ wéi	無以爲	no way to, no means to; Ch. 15; p. 131

xià	下	down, below, lower to go down, to descend; Ch. 2
xián	絃	wiry, string-like; Ch. 7
xiàng	相	minister; Ch. 12
xiàng	象	reflection, appearance, image; Ch. 7; p. 72
xiāo	消	to disperse; Ch. 14
xiǎo	小	small, lesser, insignificant; Ch. 1
xiǎo cháng	小腸	small intestine; Ch. 6
xié	邪	evil; Ch. 11; p.98
xiè	泄	to disperse, to drain; Ch. 10
xīn	心	heart, heart-mind; Ch. 3
xīn zhǔ	心主	heart master, pericardium (*sic*); Ch. 6; p. 62-4
xíng	形	form, shape; Ch. 6
xíng	行	to walk, to move about; Ch. 7; p. 94
xiōng	胸	chest; Ch. 8
xū	虛	vacuous, deficient; Ch. 4
Xú Líng-tāi	徐靈胎	medical author who lived from 1693—1771
xué	學	to study, to learn; Ch. 11
xuè (xiě)	血	blood; Ch. 3
yān	焉	short for 於之(in it); Ch. 2; p. 29-30, 50
yán	言	words, speech to talk about, to say, to speak; Ch. 6; p. 60, 61
yǎng	養	to nourish, support, to raise; Ch. 15; p. 131, 134

yǒu	有	there is, there are, there exists; Ch. 3; p. 34-5
yòu zhě	右者	the right one; Ch. 5; p. 52
yòu	右	right; Ch. 5
yú	於	preposition (in, on, at, etc.); Ch. 2; p. 29, 92, 116
yú	予	I, me, to give; Ch. 13
yú	愚	I, me stupid; Ch. 11; p. 98, 116-7
yù	鬱	depression, depressed deficient and stagnant; Ch. 10
yù	慾	desire, lust, passion, greed; Ch. 14
yǔ	與	and, with, together with to give, to accompany; Ch. 3; p. 35, 62, 63-4
yuán qì	原氣	original qi, source qi; Ch. 9
yuē	曰	to say (quote), speak of, to call; Ch. 6; p. 60, 61
yuè	月	month, moon; Ch. 4
zàng	藏	zang organ, depot (also written as 臟); Ch. 5; p. 55
zé	則	particle that sets up a contrast; Ch. 12; p. 107-108
zé	則	then (if. . . then. . .); Ch. 1; p. 22, 35, 93, 130, 131
zéi	賊	thief, robber, enemy; Ch. 13
Zhào Xiàn-kě	趙献可	medical author who lived from 1573—1644
zhé	折	to break; Ch. 10
zhě	者	nominalizing particle; Ch. 2; p. 29, 34, 61, 62, 78-9, 86, 92, 117-8, 130

zì	自	from, self, naturally; Ch. 13; p. 118
zōng	宗	to model; to take as a model; Ch. 13
zú	足	foot; Ch. 6
zuǒ	左	left; Ch. 5
zuǒ zhě	左者	the left one; Ch. 5; p. 52
zuò	坐	to sit; Ch. 7
zuò	作	to regard as, to take for; Ch. 15; p. 132

Resources

Reading List

Outline of Classical Chinese Grammar by Edwin G. Pulleyblank (University of Washington Press, 1998)

ABC Etymological Dictionary of Old Chinese by Axel Schuessler (University of Hawaii Press, 2006)

A Practical Dictionary of Chinese Medicine by Nigel Wiseman (Paradigm Publications, 1998)

A Dictionary of the Huang Di Nei Jing Su Wen by Paul Unschuld and Hermann Tessenow (University of California Press, 2008)

Internet Resources

Taiwan's Ministry of Education Chinese Dictionary: http://dict.revised.moe.edu.tw/ (Chinese only)

Rick Harbaugh's free online etymological dictionary: http://www.zhongwen.com

Interact with the author and other readers of this book. http://www.windstonepress.com

Printed in the United States
145597LV00001B/130/P

9 780982 321201